# Voyages

## The Laidlaw Reading Program · LEVEL 13

William Eller
Kathleen B. Hester

Roger Farr
DayAnn McClenathan
Mary Drew Metler
Nancy Lee Roser
Margaret A. Sloan

**LAIDLAW BROTHERS · PUBLISHERS**
A Division of Doubleday & Company, Inc.

**RIVER FOREST, ILLINOIS**

Irvine, California          Chamblee, Georgia          Dallas, Texas          Toronto, Canada

# Acknowledgments

Abingdon Press for "Josie's Handful of Quietness" by Nancy C. Smith. From JOSIE'S HANDFUL OF QUIETNESS by Nancy C. Smith. Copyright © 1975 by Abingdon. By permission of the publishers.

Addison-Wesley Publishing Company, Inc. for "His Inventions Saved Lives" by Robert C. Hayden. Adapted from EIGHT BLACK AMERICAN INVENTORS, © 1972, by Robert C. Hayden, an Addisonian Press Book, by permission of Addison-Wesley Publishing Company, Inc.

(Acknowledgments continued on page 415.)

Project Director: Ralph J. Cooke
Senior Editor: Helen W. Crane
Staff Editor: Janette Pralle Marcus
Production Director: LaVergne G. Niequist
Production Associate: Angela Zabransky
Art Director: Gloria Muczynski
Photo Researcher: William A. Cassin
Cover Art: Tak Murakami

Illustrators: Beatrice Darwin (p. 135); Kees de Kiefte (pp. 152–164); Bert Dodson (pp. 230–244); Pat Doyle (pp. 7, 105, 165, 219, 289, 349); Monroe Eisenberg (p. 245); Pamela Ford (pp. 290–292); Hal Frenck (pp. 38–51, 220–229); David Kingham (pp. 182, 183); Gordon Laite (pp. 320–329); Frank Larocco (p. 117); Don Loehle (pp. 120–134); Bob Masheris (pp. 330, 331); Al Pucci (pp. 184–205, 211); Sandy Rabinowitz (pp. 136–151); Ted Rand (pp. 84–104, 350–404); Joe Rogers (pp. 252–257, 405–414); Den Schofield (pp. 106–113); Douglas Snow (pp. 302–307); Bill Steinel (pp. 308–319); David Stone (pp. 8–36); George Ulrich (pp. 52–83, 286, 287)

Photographers: Alfa Studio (p. 336); The American Museum of Natural History (pp. 338, 343); Aspen BOLD (pp. 214, 217 *top right*); The Bettmann Archive (p. 171 *left*); Estate of Margaret Bourke-White (pp. 265, 278 *right*); Estate of Margaret Bourke-White © Time Inc. (pp. 258, 268, 273, 279, 281); The Cleveland Museum of Art, Gift of Mrs. Albert A. Levin (pp. 271, 278 *left*); Dr. E. R. Degginger (pp. 334 *third from top, fourth from top*, 335 *top, third from top*); A. Devaney, Inc. (p. 37); De Wys, Inc. (p. 293); Eastman Kodak Company (pp. 246–251); John Ebeling/Tom Stack & Associates (pp. 209, 210); Paul Freytag/ZEFA (p. 208 *top*); Grant Heilman (pp. 334 *top, bottom right*, 335 *bottom left*); Historical Pictures Service (pp. 173, 174, 332 *left*); Dr. Selina T. Johnson (pp. 345, 346); Gerolf Kalt/ZEFA (p. 206); Russ Kemp/Lizzadro Museum (p. 332 *right*); Janette Marcus (p. 257); L. David Mech (pp. 114–119); Mrs. Garrett A. Morgan, Jr. (pp. 282–288); Photri (pp. 166, 169, 170, 171 *right*); T. W. Putney/Photo Stock Library (p. 208 *bottom*); Root Resources (pp. 334 *second from top*, 335 *bottom right, second from top, fourth from top*); Elliott V. Smith (pp. 212, 213, 217 *left, bottom right*, 218); Tom Stack & Associates (pp. 334 *bottom left*, 337); Ron Testa/Field Museum of Natural History (p. 348); UPI/Compix (pp. 178–181, 301 *right*); Wide World (pp. 294, 299, 301 *left*)

ISBN 0-8445-3822-1

Copyright © 1984, 1980 by
**Laidlaw Brothers, Publishers**
A Division of Doubleday & Company, Inc.

PRINTED IN THE UNITED STATES OF AMERICA

3456789 10 11 12 13 14 15     876

# Contents

# Hold Fast to Dreams

# There the Grass Grows Soft

# Strike Out Strong

# One Morning for Pleasure

# Through the Finish Line

# Book-Length Story

6

Hold Fast to Dreams

# Josie's Handful of Quietness

by Nancy Covert Smith

Josie splashed the last of the soapy water from the bucket onto the kitchen floor. Sitting back on her heels, she swiped her long, black hair from her sweaty cheeks and smiled at Maria and Carlos. Her baby brother and little sister sat cross-legged on the table, watching her, yet out of her way.

Maria pulled her two sucking fingers from her mouth. "We get down now, Josie?"

"Not yet. I still have to rinse. It will not take long. This floor is old. It slopes so the water runs out the back door without my help."

Josie bent back to her job of trying to scrub away years of cooking grease from the bare, gray boards. The job was too hard for a twelve-year-old girl.

Carlos should have been in bed for his nap. The only reason he was not crying was because she had already given him his afternoon bottle. He sucked peacefully, his brown cheeks pumping, his round, black eyes following her movements on the floor.

Maria's small chest swelled to push out a big sigh.

Josie smiled. "I will hurry, Maria. Just watch Carlos a little longer. If you do, I will play ball outside with you while he is sleeping. OK?"

"*Sí,*" Maria cried with a quick smile. She turned on her belly and slid from the table. "I will find the ball."

"Maria!" Josie reached to grab her sister, but Maria was already running out the door. Josie called after her, "I told you, watch Carlos!"

Behind Josie, a crash. Then the baby's screams. Josie twisted to find Carlos facedown on the floor. A stream of milk followed the rinse water out the back door.

"Oh, Carlos." Josie bent to pick him up. Then she saw the milk stream turning pink as blood from somewhere joined the current. "Oh, Carlos, *niño* . . . baby." Quickly she turned him over. Under him lay the broken bottle. Blood smeared together with tears and dirt on his face.

He fought Josie with frightened, flying fists as he was lifted up. "Ahhhhhh . . ."

"Shush, *niño*. Let me see."

The baby only doubled his efforts. "Ahhhhhh . . ."

Josie felt tears sting her own eyes. "Don't cry. Don't cry." She did not know if the words were for herself or for Carlos.

Maria had come back to stand in the doorway, her fingers stuck in her mouth, her eyes wide with fright.

Josie yelled at her above the baby's screams. "It is your fault. Bad girl. You ran away."

Maria's face twisted as she began to cry. "Maria sorry."

"It is too late for sorry now."

Maria ran to Josie and flung herself against Josie's back. "I am sorry." Carlos screamed in Josie's arms. What should she do? There was no one but her. No one to ask. No one to help.

If only the children would be quiet, perhaps then she could think. If only her mother were home instead of working the field. If only she knew someone who could help. But who was there?

Then she thought of the farm down the road. There must be someone there. Yes, she would go see.

Standing up, she dragged the end of her T-shirt across Carlos' face to wipe away some of the blood and dirt. Then, holding Carlos on her hip with one arm and pulling Maria after her with the other hand, she pushed backward out the screen door. Carefully, she helped Maria down the broken step of the porch before urging her into a run. The road was a one-lane blacktop. She dropped Maria's hand so she could hold the struggling baby with both arms. "Run now. Keep up."

Maria needed no encouragement. The hot tar on the road made her pick up her bare feet quickly. To the rhythm of her running she chanted, "I am sorry, Josie. I am sorry."

At first Josie did not hear her. She was busy scanning the field across the road for signs of her mother, even though she knew she was in the east field planting today. But finally, when she stopped to shift Carlos to the other side, Maria's cries broke through to her. Maria's turned-up face quivered so pitifully, Josie tugged one of the black braids and said, "It is OK."

Once forgiven, Maria quieted to soft sobs as they began to run again.

Since the two houses were separated by a huge orchard, they had been running past rows and rows of apple trees. Now, as they came to the end of the grove of trees, Josie cut across the driveway and through the front yard. She felt soft grass under her shoes and noticed pink flowers, but she could not take time to look at them or to think about the strangers who lived here. If she did, she could not be so bold as to ask for help.

She half dragged, half helped Maria up the porch steps. Their feet thudded down the long wooden porch. Carlos' screams worked like a doorbell. Already the door was opening, and a man was reaching out.

Gratefully, Josie gave up her heavy load and followed the man into a big, white kitchen. Out of habit, she pulled Maria to her to keep her out of trouble.

The man did not ask questions. He put the baby on the counter, searching to find the source of the blood. Carlos had grown tired, so his cries had begun to weaken. The man was able to examine the swollen lip. Opening a drawer, he took a clean dish towel, wet the edge of it in cold water, and gently placed it on Carlos' face. Speaking in a deep, rumbly voice, he turned his head to look through the lower part of his glasses. "Hey, fella, what happened to you? Take a fall, did you? Well, it doesn't seem to be too bad. A little ice should fix you up."

For the first time the old man seemed to notice Josie and Maria. "Girl, look in the refrigerator freezer and get me some ice cubes."

Josie set Maria firmly on a chair and walked to the big, square refrigerator on the other side of the kitchen.

"Give the handle a hard pull, girl, or it won't open. It's getting old and reluctant to work, like me."

Josie tugged the door open and found the ice-cube tray. The man wrapped a piece of ice in the dish towel. He set Carlos up and supported him with his arm while he applied the cold to the puffy lip.

The emergency past, the man slowly looked the girls over from head to toe.

Josie felt the squashiness of her sneakers, knew her cutoff jeans were damp from the mopping and that her T-shirt was bloodstained and dirty. Not a very good appearance when meeting a new neighbor. Her hands smoothed Maria's braids.

"Don't think I know you children. You from the camp?"

"No. Well, yes."

"You sound confused."

Josie lifted her chin and set her shoulders straight. She had been asked questions like this before and did not like them. "I mean, yes, my mother and father, they work in the fields, but no, we do not live in the camp. We live in the house on the other side of your orchard."

"The old Miller place. Mr. Welter rent it to you?"

Josie resented strangers who asked questions, but this man had been good to Carlos, so she had better be polite. "Yes, my father likes our family to be alone."

"I often wondered how Roy Welter decided who got the houses and who got the shacks when you migrants arrived for the summer."

At the word "migrant" Josie looked down at her dirty sneakers. She did not like being called a migrant in that way. Migrants were Mexican-American farm laborers. This man said "migrant" in a way that made it unpleasant.

The old man must have noticed her resentment because he said, "No harm meant. It's just that so many of my apples get stolen by your people. I wouldn't mind the windfalls, but when the workers pull them off the trees before they're ripe and throw them on the ground, I don't like it. That's waste. I work hard to make a living."

Josie just said, "If Carlos is all right, we will go now."

"Oh, he's all right. More frightened than anything. There's a cut on his lip, and it's going to stay swollen for a while, but I don't think it needs stitches."

Josie picked the baby up. "Thank you."

She felt the man's hand on her shoulder. "I hurt your feelings, didn't I?"

"It does not matter."

"Sure it matters. I'm an old man who talks before he thinks. I had no right to lump all you people together and call you all thieves."

Josie stared straight ahead.

"Just a minute." The man shuffled out to a back porch. Josie noticed he had a limp. One leg was stiff. He came back with three popsicles. "Remembered I had these in the big freezer. Make your brother's mouth feel cool. He'll like it better than the plain ice."

"No, thank you. You have already done enough."

"Don't be pigheaded, girl. I'm trying to say I'm sorry." He unwrapped the red treat and handed it to Carlos. The baby leaned forward eagerly, holding out his hands. When the man stooped to hand one to Maria, Josie looked sternly at the little girl, but the treat was too good to refuse. Maria looked away from Josie and smiled at the man. She took the popsicle and said politely, "*Gracias.*"

Josie firmly refused hers. The old man grunted and took it for himself. "Come on. We'll eat them on the porch swing. Then the drips won't matter."

Josie could see there was nothing she could do but follow the man out the door. He took Maria into his lap as soon as they sat down on the swing. She went gladly. A red popsicle was all it took to win *her* as a friend.

Carlos soon forgot about his accident. As the swing swayed, he leaned against Josie's chest. His eyelids drooped, and he stopped licking the melting popsicle and started sucking it. She felt a stream of sticky cherry juice drip off his elbow onto her knee.

The old man talked to Maria. "Can you tell me your name?"

Maria ducked her head shyly. "Maria."

"Maria what?"

"García."

"Maria García. That is a beautiful name."

Maria giggled and leaned her head against the man's chest.

16

"And how old are you, Maria García?"

Maria giggled again.

Josie slapped at the little girl's brown leg. "It is not nice to laugh at people. Politely answer the man's question."

Maria held up four fingers, then said, "You rumble inside when you talk." She put her ear back on the man's chest. "Talk, please."

The man laughed and squeezed Maria tightly to him.

Josie watched them and thought, Maybe I have been too cross. Maybe I have not been fair. She said, "My name is Josie."

The man held out his hand to her like she was an adult. "Glad to meet you. My name is Glenn Curtis."

They swung a few minutes in silence.

Thinking she should make conversation, she asked, "Do you live here alone?"

Mr. Curtis cleared his throat. Josie saw his chin begin to quiver in just the way Maria's had after Carlos' fall. When he looked at her, his faded blue eyes were full of great sadness. "I've lived alone for over a year now. Mary, my wife, died a year ago spring, just before the apple blossoms came on. She always liked blossom time. Washed the dishes looking out the window at them. When the wind blew and the petals dropped, she said it looked like a shower of snow in the spring. 'Come see them, Glenn,' she would call, as if I didn't see enough of them working in the orchard every day."

He stopped talking. Josie thought he had got lost in his memories. She sat quietly. Carlos dropped to sleep, and Maria soon followed. Josie and the old man were alone, held together by the weight of the sleeping children.

What could she say to this man who lived alone in a big house with a big, white kitchen where popsicles were kept for everyday treats? She could think of nothing else, so she said, "You have pretty flowers."

"You like flowers? Just wait till this summer when my marigolds bloom. Yellow flowers everywhere. I'll give you some to plant in your yard."

Josie thought of the small square of packed-down dirt on either side of the cracked sidewalk that was supposed to be their front yard. In one corner, a trumpet vine wound around the wire fence. In the other corner, deep tracks from their truck discouraged even weeds from growing. She shook her head. "I do not think they will grow anywhere in our yard."

"Sure they will if I show you how. You see, I save the seeds each fall after the flowers die. Then, in the spring, I scatter them in every direction. All up and down the ditch banks. The strong ones take root, grow, and bloom. You wait and see, Josie García, marigolds will bloom for you, too."

Mr. Curtis smiled at her. Slowly she smiled back.

Abruptly she remembered her manners. "I should go now. You have things to do, and I must start the supper so Mama can finish it when she comes home."

"I don't have anything to do, Josie. It doesn't take much for one person to get along. I'll walk you home. You carry Carlos, and I'll bring Maria."

Josie stood up and shifted Carlos until she could carry him comfortably. She waited until Mr. Curtis got stiffly to his feet.

On the road she paced her walk to his limp. Quietly, so they would not waken the little ones, they talked. He pointed out the different kinds of trees to her as they

passed the rows of the orchard. "Red Delicious . . .
Golden Delicious . . . Stayman Red . . ."

Josie thought, What a beautiful place. I would like
to watch the apples ripen. Next spring I would like to
see the apple blossoms from *my* kitchen window.

But then they came to the end of the orchard, and she
saw the house where she lived. An unpainted, rundown
house like all the other houses she had lived in. A place
to stay just long enough to get in a crop and move on.
This was the first of June. Sometime in September they
would pack and be on their way south and west, searching for a winter crop. It was foolish of her to think of
apple orchards and planting marigolds. She was a migrant, a mover. She didn't belong anywhere.

# The Wishing Star

With the children asleep, Josie bent back over the kitchen floor. Carefully she picked up the pieces of glass and scrubbed away the milk stains. Rubbing her hands on the back of her jeans, she looked around their kitchen. Not much like Mr. Curtis' large one. Theirs held a wooden table, two chairs and a bench, a small icebox, and a three-burner hot plate. Two wooden cupboards on the wall had doors that either stuck or didn't stay shut, depending on whether the day was rainy or dry. A water bucket and dipper sat on a small shelf, and a calendar from Major's Feedstore hung on the wall.

The living room wasn't much more comfortable. Along its walls stood two more chairs like the ones in the kitchen, a table with chipped varnish, and a broken-down sofa. The furniture had come with the house. They only brought with them cooking pans, blankets, clothes, Carlos' crib, some chipped plates, and other odds and ends.

Upstairs, two rooms tried to fit under the sloping roof. One was a bedroom for their father and mother and Carlos, the other for her and Maria.

Josie cleared away the bucket and scrub rag and thought about supper. She would try to make it a good one tonight. Mother and Father would come home tired. Planting was hard work.

The truck with the tomato plants had arrived yesterday at Mr. Welter's barns. Josie knew that all day her father had been driving the transplanting machine. But it was her mother whose back would ache. Her mother followed the machine, stooping, holding the plant up straight, patting the loose dirt around the plant, walking on to the next one. She never had time to straighten except at the end of a long row. Always she walked in slow rhythm, the sun on her back, and mud caked on her hands, drying and pulling at her skin.

Josie slammed a frying pan onto the hot plate. She would fry the tortillas. She would not think about how hard her parents worked on other people's farms. That kind of thinking made her hurt inside.

She would wash the windows. If her mother would not let her help in the fields, then she would keep the house clean so her mother would not have to get up early to do so much. As Josie rubbed the kitchen window with a piece of newspaper, she wondered if her mother had ever seen the blossoms on an apple tree in the spring. They did not need the calendar from Major's Feedstore. They counted time by strawberries to pick, sugar beets to hoe, tomatoes to plant. Angrily Josie flipped the tortillas, wondering what she could cook to put on them.

Later Josie sat on the porch steps, trying to keep Carlos from eating dirt from the ground. Maria had climbed up three rows on the wire fence to watch for their parents. It bowed as she swung back and forth waiting. During planting and harvest, the two children saw little of their parents. Josie was their substitute.

Maria called out, "Mama is coming."

The mother's face broke into a smile as she waved her straw hat, calling out, *"Niños . . .* children."

The little ones ran to her.

When they were all seated at the supper table, Josie told her parents all about Carlos' accident and how kind Mr. Curtis had been to them.

Maria added her word to the story. "Popsicle."

"Was it good, *hija?*" Mrs. García asked.

"*Sí.*" Maria smiled and nodded her head until her black braids bounced.

Mr. García checked Carlos' mouth. "Popsicle seems to be good medicine."

When Josie had hung the dish towels on the fence to dry, she came up on the front porch. Mrs. García sat with her feet on the top step, her head lying forward on her knees. Josie knelt behind her mother to rub the tired muscles in her neck and shoulders. "Let me work for you tomorrow, Mother. I do not mind following the planter."

Mrs. García patted Josie's hand. "No, Josie. You stay in the house, out of the fields. You do not want hands like mine."

Josie looked at her mother's rough, scarred, and stained hands. Since her mother was ten years old she had worked in the fields. She had gone to school only when she was not needed at home.

Mrs. García sighed. "No, *hija,* do not go to the fields. You go to school. Someday you will have a *good* job."

Josie sat down on the step.

Together they enjoyed the silence of the early evening. Mrs. García asked, "You like this man, Mr. Curtis, so much?"

"I think so. At first he sounded like the others, not wanting us here because we are migrants. But he is different. This man loves. I know by the way he keeps the house clean to remember his wife, by the way he talks of his orchard, by the way he plants flowers, and by the way he helped Carlos."

"He sounds like a busy man. You will not bother this Mr. Curtis too much."

"He is lonely, too, Mama."

"Why should a man with so much be lonely?"

"I do not know all the reason for his sadness, but his eyes see something they do not want to see, I think."

Twilight came. From the house rippled Carlos' laughter as he bounced on his father's knees. Maria joined them on the porch to lean tiredly on her mother's lap, her sucking fingers pushed into her mouth, listening to her mother's soft, comforting voice.

Mrs. García pointed out the wishing star.

Josie made a wish on it, then asked, "Mama, was there ever something you wanted very much when you were young like me?"

Mrs. García was quiet a long time, looking again at her rough hands. When she finally did speak, it was only to say, "It has been too long to remember. But you, Josie, you are young. Your life is ahead of you. Do you have dreams?"

Josie hesitated. Should she say her dream out loud? It was what she just wished on the evening star. What she wished on every evening star. Wouldn't telling it destroy any chance of making it come true? But the wanting to share it was so big, she could not keep from telling it. "Yes, Mama, I want to stay here. I do not want to move anymore. I want to go to only one school. I want to belong to a place, like Mr. Curtis belongs to his."

There was no use stopping now. She went on, "I want to go to college someday. And when I graduate, I want to be a teacher. This year I will be in junior high. In one school I could make high grades. My teacher in Florida, this spring, said I could if I really want to. And I want to, Mama. I really do."

Josie stopped. She could not believe she had actually said all those things out loud. Shocked at herself, she looked up at her mother to see what she was going to do.

Her mother said nothing, only looked at her hands.

But behind them Josie heard her father say, "So you do not like the life I give you?"

Josie whirled to find her father standing above her, his black eyes hard. "No, Father, I did not . . ."

"I do not give you diamonds for your fingers, eh, my princess?"

Josie felt her mother's hand touch her shoulder. Heard her mother's soft voice saying, "Ramón, it is only a girl's dream. Do you not dream some days?"

"I have no time for dreaming. I work hard. Only those who are lazy have the time to dream. Put Josie in the fields. Let her back ache like ours. Let her earn her way."

Josie felt her mother's grip tighten, felt herself pushed aside. Her mother stood straight in front of her husband, her own eyes blazing black. "Josie is not lazy. She is a good girl."

"Too good to work in the fields. Is that what you are telling me, Eva?"

Josie's mother shoved her toward the door. "Take Maria upstairs," she said.

Josie grabbed the little girl, who was already sobbing because of the angry voices, and held her head safely in the curve of her neck. She hurried into the house and fled up the stairs to the hot, stuffy bedroom.

As she undressed Maria, Josie let the tears wash her own face. She could still hear the angry sounds of her parents' voices. How foolish she had been to tell her dream out loud. What trouble it had caused.

As she helped Maria into her pajamas, the little girl patted her cheek. "Do not cry, Josie."

"Oh, Maria, I am a bad girl."

Maria kissed her. "Josie not bad. I love Josie."

Josie laid the child down on the bed next to the wall, then crawled in beside her.

"Josie, you are still dressed."

"I know. I will stay a minute. Shush now, go to sleep."

Josie lay quietly. Downstairs it was silent. The fighting was over. Why did she not go downstairs? Why did she lie here hiding? The day slipped completely into night. The room darkened. Josie's tears and the day's hard work urged her to sleep.

It was much later that the sound of voices in the next bedroom wakened her.

"This old man puts foolish notions in Josie's head?"

"No, Ramón. Josie burst tonight like a tomato that lies too long in the sun. She has been thinking this dream long, I am sure."

"I do not understand this, Eva."

"Times are changing, Ramón. Josie sees this. She learns the new ways in the school."

"Then we should keep her at home."

"No, our children, they will search for a new way, a way different than ours."

Josie heard noises of her father moving about the room. "I cannot sleep. The room, it is too hot. I will walk." Josie heard him cross the room and then shuffle to a stop. "Eva, I know only our way."

"I know."

A small silence and then he said, "Eva, I am sorry I yelled at you."

"I know."

Josie waited until her father had gone down the steps and out into the night. Then she got up and began undressing. As she stood at the window, she saw her father's shadow moving in the moonlight. Always he was sorry after he yelled at them. She understood and did not resent him. When he was worried, his mind seemed to close up.

They could not stay here. She would not speak again of college. There would be no marigolds. Josie lay down again beside Maria and put her arm around the little girl. Then she covered them both with the sheet. The spring night was beginning to turn cool.

# A Place to Belong

The tomato planting was finished. Carlos' lip was healing. Josie continued her job as substitute mother. The days were much the same, filled with work and the children and otherwise being alone. She wished often for someone to talk to.

One morning the sun shone through the window to waken her, and she lay blinking against its brightness. As she collected her thoughts for the day, she remembered that on her walk back from Mr. Curtis' place the day of the accident, he had pointed out some wild asparagus. After breakfast dishes and washing some clothes, she would walk to the spot on the ditch bank and see if there might be enough stalks to pick for supper.

With Carlos on her hip and Maria by her side, they went out into the quiet morning. Only Maria's chattering and the sound of a cardinal broke the stillness. The country was such a silent place to live, she thought, especially when you knew no one except your family.

Workers were bent over in the fields, replanting by hand the spots where the first tomatoes, machine planted, had not survived the shock of transplant. Josie could not pick out her own mother and father. They were too far away, and the sun was too bright.

Josie found the asparagus patch. "See, Maria, there is plenty." But though Maria bent down and looked hard, she could not see the green spears hiding in the tall grass.

Josie handed her a paper bag. "Sit down with this. I will pick them, and you may put them inside the bag."

They were busy gathering and did not hear Mr. Curtis walk to the edge of the road and look down where they knelt on the ditch bank. "Well," he rumbled, "seems we have two minds with but a single thought."

Josie stood up. "Oh, I am sorry. Am I taking the asparagus from you?"

Mr. Curtis laughed. "No, what grows wild is for those who find it. There's plenty for both of us, I imagine."

When Josie had gathered all there was, she climbed back to the road and dropped some of the fresh spears into the pan Mr. Curtis carried.

"Thank you, girl. Season's almost over, so we'll have to let the rest grow up and make seed for next year." He stooped to check Carlos' lip. "You're looking well, fella. No more accidents, I see."

Josie said, "No, sir."

They stood then on the road, for a time, unable to think of anything to say. Finally Mr. Curtis said gruffly, "Well, come on. Let's walk back to my place. I haven't had breakfast yet. You can all have some milk and cookies while I have my eggs."

Josie grinned and turned the children toward the farm. Talking with him again would be much better than going back to their empty kitchen.

While the kettle boiled for Mr. Curtis' coffee, he showed them through the house. Josie liked best the big upstairs bedroom that had been Janny's. Janny was Mr. Curtis' grown-up daughter. The room was bright and airy, its two windows opened to the morning. Outside the robins and the cardinals could be heard calling. Pictures from Janny's high-school years covered the walls. It was a room where a little girl had grown into a woman. It was not like Josie's own small room, where only a picture torn from a magazine hung on a nail.

"Forty-five years Mary and I lived here. It's been a good home. Still is." He dusted off Janny's graduation picture with his sleeve. "Just the evenings sometimes get lonely. Did you ever notice that, Josie? In the summer around twilight, how sad you feel when you hear the croak of the frogs and the call of the night birds?"

Josie nodded. Yes, she knew. And she could have told him of the loneliness of the Gulf shore and of the desert. It is people who keep back loneliness, she thought, wherever you are.

Mr. Curtis hungrily ate the bacon and eggs. When he finished, he rubbed his hands down his pants legs and sighed, "Only thing I've learned to cook right. So I eat my fill every morning and hope for the best the rest of the day."

Josie dried dishes as Mr. Curtis washed them. When they finished, he said, "I've got to see to some repairs on my fruit stand before I open it for the summer. Got time to stay and hand me my tools?"

Josie nodded.

"You'll have to be sharp. Janny used to be the best tool-hander there was."

Josie grinned. "I'll try."

Mr. Curtis laid his hammer, nails, saw, and a few pieces of patch lumber out and was examining the winter damage to his fruit stand.

Josie watched as his eyes scanned the landscape before bending to his work. "Look, Josie, fields as far as you can see, no trees, just fields." He pointed to his own corner farm, his shade trees, his orchard, his flowers. To Josie it seemed like such a little bit of beauty against the treeless landscape.

Mr. Curtis finished the patching and began putting his tools back into their carrier; then he stopped. "How about that broken step at your house? I almost tripped on it the other day, carrying Maria. Someone ought to do something about it." He muttered, "Roy Welter sure won't be troubling himself over repairs. Not when he's letting all the buildings and shacks on his farms rot down."

As they got near the house, they saw the washing Josie had hung out earlier.

"Been busy as a bee, I see."

Josie nodded.

Mr. Curtis spread out his tools again. "You little ones stay out of the way."

Maria and Carlos watched wide-eyed. Finally Josie sat down nearby and pulled Carlos onto her lap.

Mr. Curtis glanced at her over the top of his glasses. "You're quite a little mother, Josie. How long have you been taking care of the children?"

Josie shrugged. "So long I do not remember not doing it. Mostly only the summers, though. In the winter the work is not so plentiful. Then I go to school part of the time, and Mother stays with Maria and Carlos."

"You don't mind?"

Josie felt a pain as the thought of the other night came to her mind—the night she had made her father angry. She said softly, "Mother is the one who works hard. I only do a little."

Mr. Curtis stopped his pounding and looked at Josie. "You're all right, girl. Kind of remind me of Janny when she was your age. Janny used to stay right with me in the orchard. Like I said, handing me things, helping out. Sure missed her when she left."

"She does not live near here?"

"No, she went away to college, got married. They live in New York now. She plays the organ there at one of the big churches."

"That sounds nice."

"It is, I suppose. We all have to do what we like, I guess. Take you, Josie. What do you want to do when you grow up?"

"Nothing," Josie said softly.

"Come on now, every girl has dreams. Don't be ashamed of your dreams, Josie."

Josie could not answer this. Tears were running down her face and making damp stains on Carlos' undershirt, and she did not want Mr. Curtis to know that she was crying.

At the silence Mr. Curtis glanced up from his work. When he saw the tears, he moved to Josie. Letting his stiff leg hang down to the step he was fixing, his strong arms lifted both Josie and Carlos onto his lap.

Josie forgot she was twelve years old and almost in junior high school. She buried her head in Mr. Curtis' warm shoulder and let the tears continue falling. He said nothing, only patted a comforting rhythm on her shoulder.

When at last she lay silent, he said gruffly, but tenderly, "What did I say wrong, girl?"

With quiet sobs breaking the sentences into bits, Josie told Mr. Curtis her dream to stay in one place, to go to school, to someday be a teacher. She told him about her parents. "They work hard. They try so hard. And I hurt them."

Mr. Curtis cleared his throat several times before he spoke. "It's never wrong to seek something better, Josie.

I'm not saying you didn't hurt your parents. You probably did. We parents have a way of getting hurt when we can't do everything for our children we would like to do. But your wish isn't unreasonable. It's what young people want. A home. A future.''

As Josie raised her head from Mr. Curtis' shoulder, she saw his eyes fill with sadness as they had that other day. He murmured, ''It's what old folks want, too. A home. A future.''

He was quiet a long time. Then he roused himself to point to the southwest. ''Right over there, Josie, used

to be a big woods of oak, ash, and maple trees. They're what brought the squirrels. I used to hunt them in the fall. Janny, Mary, and I picked wild flowers there in the spring." He pointed to the other side of the house. "Over there was a pear orchard. Always full of sweet, yellow pears. And there, on back by the creek, another woods. That one was filled with dogwood. The whole thing pink and white with blossoms in the spring. Prettiest sight you've ever seen.

"We had neighbors in all these houses around here. Kids, grown-ups, everybody used to get together for baseball in my corner pasture on a Sunday afternoon. We'd get together for bellings after weddings. Those were good times, Josie. Good times." His hand trembled as it rubbed his face.

Josie asked shyly, "What is a belling?"

"Never heard of a belling? Well, when a couple would get married, all the neighbors would sneak down to their house on the wedding night. They'd have bells, horns, pans, and spoons and surround the house. Then, at the same time, we'd all start making noise. Kept it up till the couple turned on the lights and came out on the porch. They always acted surprised, but inside was always cakes and pies and sandwiches."

Josie grinned.

Mr. Curtis grinned back, but then he said, "It's all gone now. Neighbors moved away. Kids grown. Old friends passed on. Small farms don't pay anymore, they say. People want too much, I guess. Not content with a few comforts, they want to own everything.

"Leastwise Roy Welter buys everything. One farm after another. Bulldozes the woods down. Takes out all the fence rows where the pheasants and rabbits live, so there's nothing but fields and more fields. He says he doesn't want anything standing in the way of his big machinery.

"I'm the last one. I hang on to my handful of quietness, but I feel the fields closing in. He's waiting. One day those bulldozers are going to get my place, Josie. I'm just a fool, Roy Welter thinks. Just an old man in his way." He patted Josie one more time and set her back on the step.

As Josie watched him bend slowly over his job because of his stiff leg, she realized that she wasn't the only one to have a dream. Maybe Mr. Curtis did not understand how it was to always be going to a new school. Maybe he did not know how it was to be stared at when you said your name was Josie García. Maybe he did not know the hurt of standing alone on the playground because you did not have a friend. But he did know what it was like to be afraid. Because he, too, was afraid of not having a place to belong. In this way they were alike.

She stood up. "You will stay for lunch, please?"

Mr. Curtis had his memories put back into place by this time. He smiled at Josie. "That would be nice. I want to see if you're a better cook than I am. I can't seem to get the hang of much except fried eggs."

Josie hurried inside to search the cupboards for something to feed her guest. From outside she heard the steady pounding of the hammer. "A handful of quietness," Mr. Curtis had said. What a nice thought that was. And it seemed right for the way he felt about his farm. She looked down at her hands holding a pan and a can of beans. "Will there be a handful of quietness for me?"

## Dreams

Hold fast to dreams
For if dreams die
Life is a broken-winged bird
That cannot fly.

Hold fast to dreams
For when dreams go
Life is a barren field
Frozen with snow.

Langston Hughes

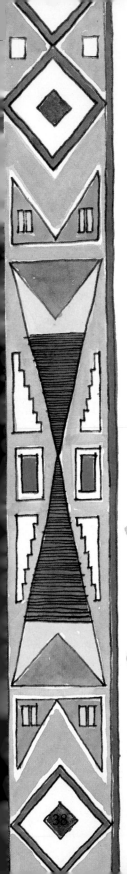

# THE MEDICINE BAG

by Virginia Driving Hawk Sneve

My kid sister Cheryl and I always bragged about our Sioux grandpa, Joe Iron Shell. Our friends, who lived in the city and only knew about Indians from movies and TV, were impressed by our stories. Maybe we exaggerated and made Grandpa and the reservation sound glamorous, but when we returned home after our yearly summer visit to Grandpa, we always had some exciting tale to tell.

We usually had a real Sioux article to show our listeners. One year Cheryl had new moccasins that Grandpa had made. On another visit he gave me a small, round, flat, rawhide drum that was decorated with a painting of a warrior riding a horse. He taught me a real Sioux chant to sing while I beat the drum with a leather-covered stick that had a feather on the end. That really made an impression!

We never showed our friends Grandpa's picture. Not that we were ashamed of him, but we knew the glamorous tales we told didn't go with the real thing. Our friends would have laughed at the picture, because Grandpa wasn't tall and stately like TV Indians. His hair wasn't in braids, but hung in stringy, gray strands on his neck. He was our great-grandfather, and he lived all by himself in a part log, part tar-paper shack on the Rosebud Reservation in South Dakota. So when Grandpa came to visit us, I was so embarrassed I could've died.

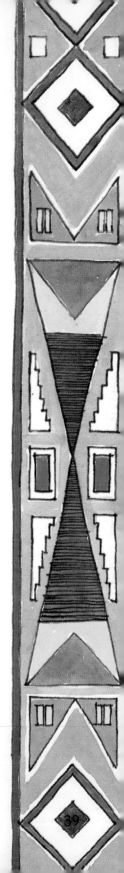

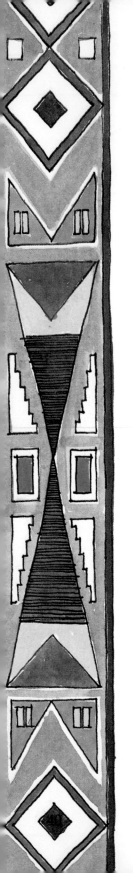

There are a lot of yippy little dogs in our neighborhood, but they usually bark singly at the mail carrier from the safety of their own yards. Now it sounded as if a whole pack of mutts was barking together in one place.

I got up and walked to the curb to see what was causing all the fuss. About a block away I saw a crowd of little kids yelling, with the dogs yipping and growling around someone who was walking down the middle of the street.

I watched the group as it slowly came closer and saw that in the center of the strange parade was a man wearing a tall black hat. He'd pause now and then to peer at something in his hand and then at the houses on either side of the street. I felt cold and hot at the same time as I recognized him. "Oh, no!" I whispered. "It's Grandpa!"

I stood on the curb, unable to move, even though I wanted to run and hide. Then I got mad when I saw how the yipping dogs were growling at Grandpa's baggy pant legs and how wearily he poked them away with his cane. "Stupid mutts," I said as I ran to rescue him.

When I hollered at the dogs to get away, they put their tails between their legs and scattered. The kids ran to the curb, where they watched me and the old man.

"Grandpa," I said and felt pretty dumb when my voice cracked. I reached for his beat-up old tin suitcase, which was tied shut with a rope. But he set it down right in the street and shook my hand.

"*Hau*, Grandchild," he greeted me in Sioux.

All I could do was stand there with the whole neighborhood watching and shake his leathery, brown hand. I saw how the gray hair straggled from under his big black hat, which had a drooping feather in its crown. His wrinkled black suit hung like a sack over his stooped frame. As he shook my hand, his coat fell open to expose a bright-red satin shirt with a beaded bolo tie under the collar. His getup wasn't out of place on the reservation, but it sure was here; and I wanted to sink right through the pavement.

"Hi," I muttered with my head down. I tried to pull my hand away when I felt his bony hand trembling, and I looked up to see the exhaustion in his face. I felt like crying. I couldn't think of anything to say, so I picked up Grandpa's suitcase, took his arm, and guided him up the driveway to our house.

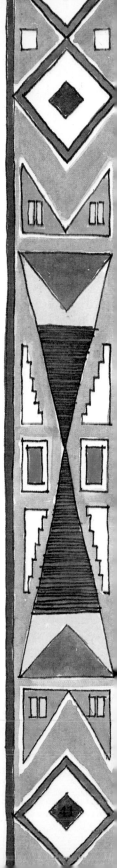

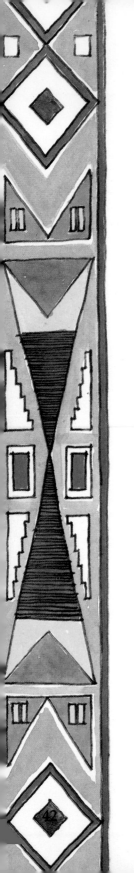

Mom was standing on the steps. I don't know how long she'd been watching, but her hand was over her mouth, and she looked as if she couldn't believe what she saw. Then she ran to us.

"Grandpa," she gasped. "How in the world did you get here?"

She checked her move to hug Grandpa, and I remembered that such a show of affection is unseemly to the Sioux and would embarrass him.

"*Hau,* Marie," he said as he shook Mom's hand. She smiled and took his other arm.

As we supported him up the steps the door banged open, and Cheryl came bursting out of the house. She was all smiles and was so glad to see Grandpa that I felt awfully guilty.

"Grandpa!" she hollered. "You came to see us!"

Grandpa smiled, and Mom and I let go of him as he stretched out his arms to my 10-year-old sister, who was still young enough to be hugged.

"*Hau,* little girl," he greeted her, and then fell in a heap on the floor.

He had fainted. Mom and I helped him into her sewing room, where we had a spare bed.

After we had Grandpa on the bed, Mom suggested calling the doctor. "You make Grandpa comfortable, Martin," she said with a sigh.

Grandpa was so skinny that his coat slipped off easily. When I loosened his tie and opened his shirt collar, I felt a small leather pouch that hung from a thong around his neck. I left it alone and started to remove his boots. They were tight, and he moaned as I put pressure on his legs to jerk them off.

I put the boots on the floor and saw why they fit so tight. Each one was stuffed with money. I looked at the bills that lined the boots and started to ask about them, but Grandpa's eyes were closed again.

Mom came back with a basin of water. "The doctor thinks Grandpa is suffering from heat exhaustion," she explained as she bathed his face. Mom gave a big sigh. "Oh, Martin. How do you suppose he got here?"

We found out later. Grandpa was angrily sitting up in bed while Mom tried to feed him some soup.

"Tonight you let Marie feed you, Grandpa," said my dad, who had gotten home from work just as the doctor was leaving. "You're not really sick." He gently pushed Grandpa back against the pillows. "According to the doctor you just got too tired and hot after your long trip."

Grandpa calmed down, and between sips of soup he told us of his journey. Soon after our visit to him, Grandpa decided that he would like to see where his only living descendants lived and what our home was like. Besides, he admitted, he was lonesome.

I knew everybody felt as guilty as I did—especially Mom. She was all Grandpa had left. So even after she married my dad, who's a white man and teaches in the college in our city, and after Cheryl and I were born, Mom made sure that every summer we spent a week with Grandpa on the reservation.

I never thought that Grandpa would be lonely after our visits, and none of us noticed how old and weak he had become. But Grandpa knew, and so he came to us. He had ridden on buses for two and a half days. When he arrived in the city, tired and stiff from sitting for so long, he set out, walking, to find us.

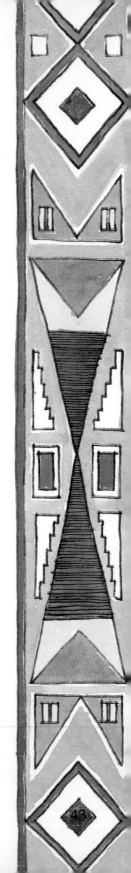

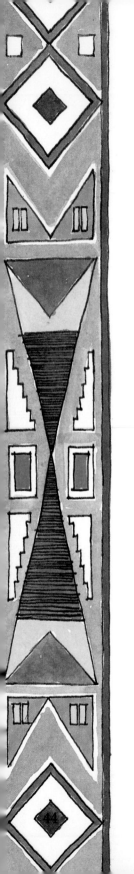

He had stopped to rest on the steps of some building downtown where a police officer found him. The officer, according to Grandpa, took him to the bus stop, waited until the bus came, and told the driver to let Grandpa out at Bell View Drive. After Grandpa got off the bus, he started walking again. But he couldn't see the house numbers on the other side when he walked on the sidewalk, so he walked in the middle of the street. That's when all the little kids and the dogs followed him.

I knew everybody felt as bad as I did. Yet I was proud of this 86-year-old man, who had never been away from the reservation, but had the courage to travel so far alone.

"You found the money in my boots?" he asked Mom.

"Martin did," she answered and roused herself to scold. "Grandpa, you shouldn't have carried so much money. What if someone had stolen it from you?"

Grandpa laughed. "I would've known if anyone tried to take the boots off my feet. The money is what I've saved for a long time—a hundred dollars. You take it now to buy groceries so that I won't be a burden to you while I am here."

"That won't be necessary, Grandpa," Dad said. "We are honored to have you with us, and you will never be a burden. I am only sorry that we never thought to bring you home with us this summer and spare you the discomfort of a long trip."

Grandpa was pleased. "Thank you," he answered. "But do not feel bad that you didn't bring me with you, for I would not have come then. It was not time." He said this in such a way that no one could argue with him. To Grandpa and the Sioux, he once told me, a thing would be done when it was the right time to do it, and that's the way it was.

"Also," Grandpa went on, looking at me, "I have come because it is soon time for Martin to have the medicine bag."

We all knew what that meant. Grandpa thought he was going to die, and he had to follow the tradition of his family to pass the medicine bag, along with its history, to the oldest male child.

"Even though the boy," he said still looking at me, "bears a white person's name, the medicine bag will be his."

I didn't know what to say. I had the same hot-and-cold feeling that I had when I first saw Grandpa in the street. The medicine bag was the dirty leather pouch I had found around his neck. "I could never wear such a thing," I almost said aloud. I thought of having my friends see it in class or at the swimming pool, and I could imagine the smart things they would say. But I just swallowed hard and took a step toward the bed. I knew I would have to take it.

But Grandpa was tired. "Not now, Martin," he said, waving his hand. "It is not time. Now I will sleep."

So that's how Grandpa came to be with us for two months. My friends kept pressuring me to let them come and see the old man, but I put them off. I told myself that I didn't want them laughing at Grandpa. But even as I made excuses, I knew that wasn't what I was afraid of.

Nothing bothered Cheryl about bringing her friends to see Grandpa. Every day after school started, there'd be a crew of openmouthed little girls or round-eyed little boys crowded around the old man on the patio, where he'd gotten in the habit of sitting every afternoon.

Grandpa would smile in his gentle way and patiently answer their questions, or he'd tell them stories of brave

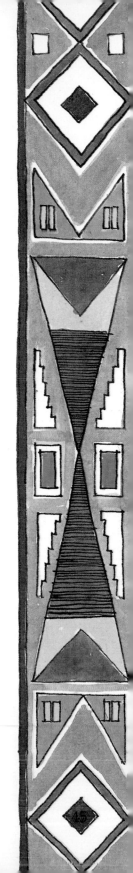

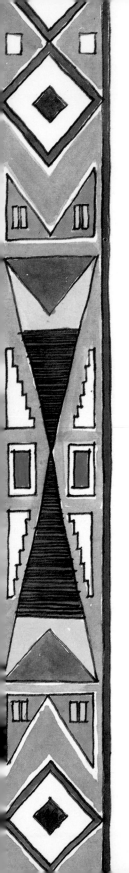

warriors, and the kids would listen in awed silence. Grandpa was great.

Finally, one day after school, my friends came home with me because nothing I could say would stop them. "We're going to see the great Indian of Bell View Drive," said Hank, who was supposed to be my best friend. "My brother has seen your grandfather three times, so he ought to be well enough to see us."

When we got to my house, Grandpa was sitting on the patio. He had on his red satin shirt, but today he also wore a fringed leather vest that was decorated with beads. Instead of boots, he had solidly beaded moccasins on his feet. Of course, he had his old black hat on—he was rarely without it. Silver strands of hair framed his face and lay over the red shirt collar.

I stared just as my friends did, and I heard one of them murmur, "Wow!"

Grandpa looked up and when his eyes met mine, they twinkled as if he was laughing inside. He nodded to me, and my face got all hot. I could tell that he had known all along I was afraid he'd embarrass me in front of my friends.

"*Hau*, boys," he greeted and held out his hand.

My buddies passed in a single file and shook his hand as I introduced them. They were so polite I almost laughed when they spoke. "How, there, Grandpa," and even a "How do you do, sir."

"You look fine, Grandpa," I said as the guys sat on the lawn chairs or on the patio floor.

"Yes," he agreed. "When I woke up this morning, it seemed the right time to dress in the good clothes. I knew that my grandson would be bringing his friends."

"You guys want some lemonade or something?" I offered. No one answered. They were listening to Grandpa as he started telling how he'd killed the deer from which his vest was made.

Grandpa did most of the talking while my friends were there. I was proud of him and amazed at how respectfully quiet my buddies were. Mom had to chase

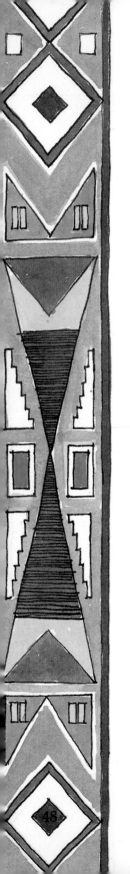

them home at suppertime. As they left, they shook Grandpa's hand again.

"Martin, he's really great!" Hank said in awe.

"Yeah! Don't blame you for keeping him to yourself."

"Can we come back?"

But after they left, Mom said, "No more visitors for a while, Martin. Grandpa won't admit it, but his strength hasn't returned. He likes having company, but it tires him."

That evening Grandpa called me to his room before he went to sleep. "Tomorrow," he said, "when you come home, it will be time to give you the medicine bag and its history."

I felt a hard squeeze from where my heart is supposed to be and was scared, but I answered, "OK, Grandpa."

All night I had strange dreams about thunder and lightning on a high hill. From a distance I heard the slow beat of a drum. When I woke up in the morning I felt like I hadn't slept at all. At school it seemed as if the day would never end, and when it finally did, I ran home.

Grandpa was in his room, sitting on the bed. The shades were down, and the place was dark and cool. I sat on the floor in front of Grandpa, but he didn't even look at me. After what seemed a long time, he spoke.

"What you will hear today is only for your ears, Martin. What you will receive is only for your hands." He fell silent, and I felt shivers down my back.

"My father in his early manhood," Grandpa began, "made a vision quest to find a spirit guide for his life. You cannot understand how it was in that time, when the mighty Sioux were first made to stay on the reservation. There was a strong need for guidance from the Great Spirit. But too many of the young people were filled with anger. They thought it was hopeless to search for a vision when the good life was gone and only the hated reservation lay ahead. But my father held to the old traditions.

"He carefully prepared for his quest with a cleansing sweat bath, and then he went alone to a high butte top to fast and pray. After three days he received his sacred dream—in which he found, after long searching, the white people's iron. He did not understand his vision of finding something belonging to the white people, for in that time they were the enemy. When he came down from the butte to cleanse himself at the stream, he found the remains of a campfire and the broken shell of an iron kettle. This was a sign that gave meaning to his dream. He took a piece of the iron for his medicine bag, which he had made of elk skin years before when preparing for the quest.

"He returned to the village, where he told his dream to the other members of the tribe. They gave him the name *Iron Shell*, but they did not understand the meaning of the dream, either. This first Iron Shell kept the piece of iron with him at all times and believed it gave him protection from the evils of those unhappy days.

"Then a terrible thing happened to Iron Shell. He and several other young men were taken from their homes by the soldiers and sent far away to a white boarding school. He was angry and lonesome for his parents and the young girl he had wed before he was taken away. At first Iron Shell resented the teacher's attempts to change him, and he did not try to learn. One day it was his turn to work in the school's blacksmith shop. As he walked into the place, he knew that his medicine bag had brought him there to learn and to work with the white people's iron.

"Iron Shell became a blacksmith and worked at the trade after he returned to the reservation. All his life he treasured the medicine bag. When he was old and I was a man, he gave it to me, for no one made the vision quest anymore."

Grandpa quit talking, and I stared in disbelief as he covered his face with his hands. His shoulders were shaking with quiet sobs, and I looked away until he began to speak again.

"I kept the bag until my son, your mother's father, had to leave us to fight in the war across the ocean. I gave him the bag, for I believed it would protect him in battle, but he did not take it with him. He was afraid that he would lose it. He died in a faraway place."

Again Grandpa was still, and I felt his sadness all around me.

He unbuttoned his shirt, exposing the leather pouch, and lifted it over his head. He held it in his hand, turning it over and over as though wanting to remember how it looked.

"In the bag," he said, opening it and removing two objects, "is the broken shell of the iron kettle, a pebble from the butte, and a piece of the sacred sage." He held the pouch upside down, and dust drifted down.

"After the bag is yours, you must put a piece of prairie sage within and never open it again until you pass it on to your son." He replaced the pebble and the piece of iron and tied the bag.

I stood up, somehow knowing I should. Grandpa slowly rose from the bed and stood upright in front of me, holding the bag before my face. I closed my eyes and waited for him to slip the thong over my head. But he spoke.

"No, you need not wear it." He placed the soft leather bag in my right hand and closed my other hand over it. "It would not be right to wear it in this time and place, where no one will understand. Put it safely away until you are again on the reservation. Wear it then, when you replace the sacred sage."

Grandpa turned and sat again on the bed. Wearily he leaned his head against the pillow. "Go," he said. "I will sleep now."

"Thank you, Grandpa," I said softly and left with the bag in my hands.

That night Mom and Dad took Grandpa to the hospital. Two weeks later I stood on the lonely prairie of the reservation and put the sacred sage in my medicine bag.

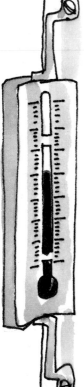

# FELICIA the CRITIC

by Ellen Conford

". . . and the current temperature is forty-nine WGVM degrees."

Felicia looked at the thermometer outside the kitchen window and shook her head.

"The current temperature is fifty-one KERSHENBAUM degrees," she informed the radio announcer, who was giving the weather report.

"Do we *have* to go through this *every morning?*" moaned her sister Marilyn.

"Have to go through what every morning?" asked Felicia, sprinkling sugar over her cold cereal.

"Felicia!" Her mother grabbed her hand as she dipped into the sugar bowl for the fourth time. "Three spoonfuls is enough!"

"*I'm* not on a diet," Felicia said, watching Marilyn shell a hard-boiled egg. "Have to go through what every morning?" she repeated.

"Marilyn," their father said, "you're not eating enough to keep an ant alive. How long are you going to stay on this ridiculous diet?"

"Every morning," Marilyn said to Felicia, "you listen to the weather forecast and say it's wrong."

"But it always is," Felicia insisted.

"Does it seem as if Marilyn's ignoring me?" Mr. Kershenbaum asked Mrs. Kershenbaum.

"It does seem that way, yes," she replied.

"Did it ever occur to you," Marilyn demanded, "that *you* might be wrong?"

"No," said Felicia.

Marilyn drummed her fingers on the table. Felicia knew that meant Marilyn was getting very angry, but she couldn't understand what she was angry about.

"Look," Marilyn began, trying to sound very patient, but not sounding patient at all, "if it *annoys* you so much that they always have the temperature wrong, *why* do you always *listen?*"

"Because I like to know what the weather's going to be," explained Felicia. Why else would you listen to the weather forecast, she wondered. Sometimes Marilyn couldn't seem to understand the simplest things.

"But if you——"

"Marilyn! Enough, please," their mother interrupted, holding up her hand. "It's much too early for this."

"Are you going to eat anything besides that hard-boiled egg?" Mr. Kershenbaum asked.

"May I have a cup of black coffee?" Marilyn asked.

"No, you may not!" her mother retorted.

"Then I'm not eating anything besides the egg," Marilyn told her father.

"Did you know that black coffee will rot your insides?" Felicia informed them.

"Felicia, please!" said her mother, putting down her coffee cup.

"Actually," said Felicia, hoping she hadn't really scared her mother, "I don't even remember where I read that. I just didn't want Marilyn to feel bad because she couldn't have coffee. Maybe I just now made it up."

"I can't stand it!" Marilyn cried, pushing her chair back from the table.

She means she can't stand me, Felicia thought. No matter what Felicia said or did these days, Marilyn couldn't seem to stand her. The thing is, her mother had said, Marilyn is very sensitive. As if that explained anything! Why did being sensitive give you the right to be nasty to other people? Who might, Felicia thought resentfully, be sensitive, too.

"You know," Felicia began helpfully, eyeing Marilyn's bright-red sweater and plaid slacks and thinking of how concerned her sister was about her looks these days, "they say that dark colors make you seem thinner."

"Ohhh!" groaned Marilyn and stalked out of the kitchen without another word.

"Felicia," her mother sighed.

"What?" asked Felicia, completely bewildered. She had made a simple suggestion about how her sister could look thinner—and that's what Marilyn wanted, or why else would she be on a diet?—and Marilyn was mad at her again.

"Forget it," her father said hopelessly.

"Can I wear my poncho?" Felicia asked.

"Oh, I think it's a little chilly for your poncho," her mother objected.

"Oh, no it's not. Please. It's fifty-one degrees," Felicia pleaded. Her aunt had knitted her a beautiful orange and brown poncho, and she had been waiting for the weather to be just right—not too warm and not too cold. "I'll be too hot in my winter coat. *Please!*"

"All right, all right," her mother gave in.

Felicia ran upstairs and flung open the door of her closet. The poncho was still in its box, carefully wrapped in white paper. Felicia lovingly stroked the fuzzy wool and unfolded it so she could hold it up in front of the mirror. She slipped it on over her head and smoothed it down in front. Gorgeous!

She stepped back to look at herself, turning around in front of the mirror. She couldn't see the back of herself as she turned, but it was what people always did when they admired the clothes they were trying on, and the movement made the fringe flutter.

She ran downstairs and grabbed her books and her lunch.

"I'm going!" she yelled to her parents.

"Wait. Let's see how you look in the poncho!" her mother called.

"Isn't it beautiful?" Felicia beamed as her parents came to the door to see her off.

She turned around again so they could admire both sides of her.

"It really is," her mother agreed.

"'Bye," she said, hugging her mother.

"Have a good day," her father said.

Felicia was sure it would be a good day. She was wearing her poncho at last, and Cheryl was going to meet her at the corner, so she would have someone to walk to school with. Sometimes Cheryl's father drove her to school, like when she had to bring her bass viol in for orchestra, and then Felicia ended up walking alone.

It wasn't that she didn't like to walk by herself. Lots of times, after school or during vacations, she went on walks alone, exploring the blocks beyond her own, hoping that she would have some sort of adventure or maybe even discover a completely uncharted block that no one had ever seen before.

But somehow, walking to school alone was different from taking a walk.

Cheryl was not at the corner when Felicia got there. Maybe Mr. Sweet had driven her to school after all. Or maybe Cheryl was sick and not even coming to school.

Felicia suddenly felt a little chilly under her poncho, and she shivered. Maybe she'd been wrong; maybe it wasn't a beautiful poncho day at all.

Then she saw Cheryl trotting up Decatur Street toward the corner. Felicia felt such a wave of relief wash over her that she wanted to grab Cheryl and hug her.

But instead she said, "You're late."

"Well, I couldn't help it," Cheryl panted, sounding a little annoyed. "I woke up late, and my mother made me practice a whole half hour anyway."

They started up Perry Street, walking slowly so Cheryl could catch her breath.

"If you got an alarm clock," Felicia suggested, "you could wake up on time."

"I have an alarm clock. I forgot to set it."

"Maybe if you put a little sign next to it, like 'RE-MEMBER TO SET ME' or something——"

"For heaven's sake, Felicia," interrupted Cheryl, "this is the first time in a whole year that I overslept." She still sounded annoyed. She must be mad at her mother for making her practice even though she was late, Felicia thought. That *is* pretty unreasonable.

But that was the way Mrs. Sweet was. Actually, Mrs. Sweet thought herself very reasonable. She talked in a cool, reasonable tone of voice, and everything she said was reasonable. But she made Cheryl do a lot of things, and Cheryl wasn't sure she wanted to do all of them.

Like taking dancing lessons and going to French class on Saturday mornings and taking ice-skating lessons and having to practice the bass viol.

Although the bass viol was Cheryl's choice, Mrs. Sweet had wanted her to learn to play the violin for the school orchestra. Once Cheryl saw the bass viol and heard the sounds it made, she was determined not to be talked out of it, and she had won. But since she had to practice a half hour every day, Felicia wasn't sure Cheryl had really won anything.

They walked the rest of the way to school without saying very much, but that was all right. Felicia loved to talk, but sometimes Cheryl didn't. And it didn't matter because they were friends. They could walk together without saying one word, and that was okay with Felicia.

The crossing guard stopped them just as they stepped off the curb to cross the street.

"Hold it there!" he ordered.

Felicia and Cheryl stepped back onto the sidewalk where they waited.

"Look at that," grumbled Felicia. "He's letting all those cars go by, and then he's going to let the other cars make their turns. There are only two of us standing here, and we were practically halfway across the street anyway."

"It doesn't seem fair," Cheryl agreed.

"It's not just that it's not fair," Felicia complained, "but it's not *efficient*, either." "Efficient" had become one of Felicia's favorite words, ever since her father had pointed out to her that there were more efficient ways of getting her room cleaned up than by throwing everything into the bottom of her closet and then hoping that she wouldn't be told to clean out the closet.

"The efficient way would be to let us cross because there are only two of us and then let those three cars turn, and then the traffic going straight wouldn't have to stop at all after that. Because," Felicia glanced nervously around, "I think we're the last ones here."

The crossing guard stopped the traffic again and waved the two girls across the street.

"You see," Felicia said, hurrying into the school yard, "he just had to stop another whole line of cars to let us cross. Not efficient."

"Hurry up," urged Cheryl, sounding annoyed again. "We're going to be late."

At lunchtime, Felicia and Cheryl sat at a table with Phyllis Brody, Lorraine Kalman, and Fern Krinsky.

"Look at that Polly George," Phyllis whispered. "Talking about her club. That's all she ever does. What's so great about her old club anyway?"

"What's so great about *any* club?" Felicia asked.

Phyllis looked at her disdainfully.

"Well, what do they do?" Felicia wanted to know. "What's the club for?"

"For?" echoed Fern. "What does it have to be for? It's a *club.*"

"Well, it should be *for* something," Felicia insisted. "You know, like stamp collecting or feeding starving children?"

"It's just a club, Felicia," Lorraine said in the same patient-but-not-really-patient tone of voice Marilyn often used with her.

"I think a club should be organized to *do* something," Felicia went on doggedly. "Or else it's not a club. It's just a group."

Phyllis and Lorraine exchanged looks.

"Anyway," Phyllis continued, glaring at Felicia, "the way she's always whispering to people makes me sick."

"Maybe it wouldn't make you sick if she whispered to you sometimes," Felicia suggested, tearing open her bag of corn chips.

Phyllis stared at her. "Eat your corn chips, Felicia," she said coldly.

But Phyllis's anger made Felicia's stomach jump. She pushed the bag of corn chips to the center of the table. "Anybody want some?" she muttered without looking up at the girls.

Nobody answered her, but Phyllis and Lorraine and Fern helped themselves to big handfuls.

"Felicia, want to trade?" Cheryl asked. "I have a bologna sandwich."

"Thanks," Felicia said gratefully. Cheryl always sensed the right thing to say.

"Here." Felicia handed Cheryl half her sandwich.

Cheryl grinned. "But you have bologna, too."

"But yours is on rye bread, and mine is on whole wheat," Felicia explained.

That wasn't really the reason. Felicia liked whole wheat bread almost as much as rye. She just wanted to trade with Cheryl today.

It made her feel better.

# The Unveiling

"Where's Mom?" Felicia asked, dropping her schoolbooks on the kitchen table.

"Shopping," said Marilyn, not even looking up from her fingernails, which she was gloomily painting "Concord Grape."

Felicia opened the refrigerator and peered inside.

"A good thing she is," commented Felicia, groping around through the shelves. "There isn't a thing in here to eat."

She took two slices of American cheese and a square of baking chocolate and put them on the table along with a jar of peanut butter and a spoon.

"You're going to get fat if you keep eating like that," Marilyn predicted.

Felicia took a spoonful of peanut butter and licked at it.

"Ohhh! How can you? Just watching you eat that makes me ill."

"Don't watch me, then," said Felicia reasonably.

"What do you think of this color?" Marilyn asked, holding up her hand so Felicia could see her nails.

The question was so unexpected that Felicia was startled. Marilyn never asked her opinion about anything, and half the time when Felicia said something to her sister, the reply was, "Who asked you?"

Felicia carefully peeled the plastic wrap off her cheese. Did Marilyn want to know the truth, or was she going to be sensitive and hurt if Felicia said she didn't like the color? Felicia sat, nibbling her cheese, hoping Marilyn would forget she'd asked.

"What do you think of this color?" Marilyn repeated. "Aren't you listening?"

"I'm listening," Felicia said calmly.

"*Well?*"

"I think," Felicia said reluctantly, "that it looks like dried blood."

"Ohhh!" Marilyn hissed. "You——"

Felicia jerked away from her sister, hitting her arm against the peanut butter jar, knocking it off the table onto the floor.

"Ohhh," groaned Felicia, looking at the mess of broken glass and peanut butter.

"You'd better clean that up before Mother gets home," Marilyn warned. Felicia thought her sister looked almost glad about the mess on the floor.

Felicia went to the broom closet to get the broom and dustpan. The narrow closet was filled to the brim with cleaning equipment, all looking as if it would tumble out if anyone tried to remove anything. Felicia tugged at the broom, catching a sponge mop as it fell out at her and shoving it back in the closet. The dustpan was on the floor, with a pail of rags and a can of floor wax on top of it. Spray cans, jars, and containers surrounded it on all sides. Carefully Felicia maneuvered things around till she could get the dustpan out.

"Whew," she breathed, forcing the closet door shut and leaning against it. "I'm tired before I've even started. What an inefficient closet."

She started to sweep up the broken glass, but it was all mixed in with the peanut butter, and Felicia realized she was smearing the stuff all over the floor.

"Ohhh!" she wailed. "Look at this!"

Marilyn looked disinterestedly. "You're making a bigger mess than before," she commented.

The front door opened. "It's me," their mother called.

"Don't come in here with bare feet!" yelled Felicia.

"I don't usually go shopping in my bare—what happened here?" Mrs. Kershenbaum asked, standing in the kitchen doorway with two bags of groceries in her arms.

"It was an accident, and I'm not doing too well getting it cleaned up."

"I can see that. Marilyn, take these bags, please, and be careful not to slip. I have three more out in the car you can help me with."

Marilyn sighed deeply and pulled herself up from her chair with a great effort. She took the bags from her mother and put them on the kitchen table.

"Wait, Felicia. I'll help you with that," her mother said. "I think you're just making it worse. Marilyn, what is that on your fingernails?"

"Concord Grape," Marilyn said.

"Remove it, please," her mother said. "You look like a vampire."

"*Mother!*"

"I thought it looked like dried blood," Felicia said.

"Maybe that's why I thought of a vampire," her mother remarked.

"*Mother,*" Marilyn repeated.

"Oh, forget it, Marilyn," her mother said. "Leave it on, leave it on. If you want to look like a vampire, that's your business. Just help me get those groceries in, please."

Grumbling, Marilyn followed her out to the car.

They came back in and plopped the bags down on the table.

"We'd better get this cleaned up first," said Mrs. Kershenbaum, taking off her coat.

She opened the broom-closet door, and the mop fell out at her. She shoved it back in, maneuvered around some cleaning supplies, and finally pulled out a big bag of sponges.

"Look, do it this way," she said, showing Felicia how to push the glass into one heap with the sponge and then wipe it all into the dustpan. "See, with the sponge you won't cut yourself, and then when the glass is all cleaned up, you can take care of the peanut butter."

"There," she said when Felicia was finished, "now we can walk in here without risk to life and limb. Where did Marilyn go? I wanted her to help me put the groceries away."

"Don't call her," Felicia said quickly. "I'll help you." She wanted an excuse to be alone with her mother. The way Phyllis, Lorraine, and Fern had talked to her at lunch had bothered Felicia all day. Even walking home with Cheryl hadn't made her forget the way she felt when Phyllis said, "Eat your corn chips, Felicia," in that cold, disdainful voice. Maybe her mother could explain why the girls had acted that way.

"So," Mrs. Kershenbaum said when Felicia finished telling her the conversation as exactly as she could remember, "you got the feeling they were mad at you."

"It was no feeling," Felicia said positively. "They were mad at me, all right. But I don't know why."

Her mother looked at her for a long time. "Are you sure," she said finally, "you don't know why? You haven't even got an idea?"

"Well," Felicia hesitated, "I told the truth. Maybe they didn't like that."

"Felicia," her mother said gently, "there's a difference between truth and opinion. The truth is facts. Opinion is what you think. You told them what you thought."

"And they didn't like that. Shouldn't I say what I think?"

Her mother frowned. "Look, if you have a great idea for something and someone comes along and says, 'Boy, what a dumb idea, this is wrong and this is wrong,' wouldn't you feel bad?"

"I guess so," Felicia said uncertainly.

"Well, you see, you tend to be a little—critical. People don't like it when you tell them all their bad points or all the things that are wrong with their ideas."

"It's bad to be critical?" asked Felicia, puzzled.

"Not that it's bad," her mother said. "But don't expect people to appreciate you when you tell them what they're doing wrong or why their plans won't work. Actually, there are people who make a career out of being critical."

"There are?"

"Sure. Critics."

"What do they do?" Felicia asked curiously.

"They read books and see plays and movies and concerts and television shows, and then they write their opinions about them. They explain what they thought was wrong and what they thought was right."

Felicia thought about this for a minute. Her mother said she tended to be critical, and there were actually people who got paid for being critical! Maybe . . .

"Maybe *I'll* be a critic some day," Felicia said thoughtfully.

"I wouldn't be surprised." Her mother grinned. "But, in the meanwhile, you might try constructive criticism."

"Constructive criticism?"

"Instead of saying, 'This is lousy, this is lousy, and this is lousy,' you point out how it could be better. See, constructive criticism is helpful. If you just tear something apart, you're being *de*structive. But if you show how it could be made better or done better, you're being *con*structive. And that's a very valuable talent to have, to be able to be a constructive critic."

A constructive critic! thought Felicia. That's what she was going to be from now on. Her parents always said that children should develop their talents. A talent should be practiced till you got better and better at it.

Well, Felicia decided, criticalness is my talent, and I ought to develop it. There is no point, her mother always advised, in trying to be something you're not. Just be the best you can at what you are.

That's what I'll do, Felicia decided. I'll be the best critic I can. A *constructive* critic.

"Do you mind," Felicia asked her mother, "if I make some constructive criticisms about the broom closet?"

"What?" asked her mother, bewildered.

"Well, I just decided I'm going to be a constructive critic, and I think there might be some ways to make the broom closet more—efficient."

"Be my guest. Any constructive criticism about *that* disaster area will be appreciated."

Felicia ran to get a magazine she had seen a couple of days ago. There was a picture in it of a "cleaning closet" that she remembered. Now if she could make her mother's broom closet look like that . . .

She found the picture and studied it for a while. Then she took a pencil and paper, and biting her lip in concentration, began to write down her ideas.

"Now," she announced to her mother a while later, "I have here some suggestions about the broom closet. Some constructive criticism."

"Not right now, dear," Mrs. Kershenbaum said absently.

"Then can I do what I wrote on the list myself?"

"Yes, go ahead."

"I need some nails and a hammer."

"In the basement."

Felicia got the hammer and the nails and took everything out of the broom closet. Then she started pounding.

"What are you doing?" her mother asked.

"Putting nails in to hang things up," Felicia replied.

"Oh. Well, be careful."

"What is that HORRIBLE NOISE?" Marilyn yelled.

"Felicia is fixing up the broom closet," her mother yelled back over the noise of the pounding hammer.

"She'll probably break it," Marilyn said sourly, standing at the kitchen door to watch her sister.

"You can't break a broom closet," Felicia muttered, concentrating on her project.

"*You* could," retorted Marilyn. "Which one do you like best?" she asked her mother, holding up one hand with four fingernails painted different colors.

"That one," said her mother, pointing to the one pale fingernail on Marilyn's hand.

"I didn't put any polish on that one!" Marilyn wailed.

"Yes. I like that," her mother said firmly.

Felicia worked for almost an hour. When she was finished, she stood back to survey the job. It's good, she thought warmly. It's really good! It's neat and organized and—efficient. She closed the door of the closet.

"I'm done," she announced. "Everybody come look."

Her father had come home while she was working and came into the kitchen now to see what she'd been doing.

"I'm here," her mother said, turning around to look.

"You, too, Marilyn!" Felicia yelled.

"I do not have a burning interest in broom closets!" Marilyn yelled back. "Hold the unveiling without me."

"Come on, Marilyn," Felicia insisted. "You were the one who said I'd break the closet."

"Oh, for heaven's sake," Marilyn complained, but she came, finally, into the kitchen, too.

"Ready?" Felicia asked. "Da dum!" She flung open the door of the broom closet.

"It's gorgeous!" her mother gasped. "Felicia, it's wonderful."

"This is not our broom closet," declared Mr. Kershenbaum. "This is certainly not the broom closet I know and hate."

Felicia had put nails in the walls to hang up all the mops and brooms that had hooks on their handles. The ones that didn't have hooks hung with their handles downward on the wall, with two nails forming a sort of holder for them. The cleaning supplies were neatly arranged on the floor of the closet, and the sponges were evenly stacked on the one small shelf at the top. Felicia had folded all the rags and put them next to the sponges.

"I can't get over it," her mother said admiringly. "I've been meaning to do something about that closet for years . . ."

Felicia beamed with pride.

"Would you say that was constructive?" she asked her mother.

"Extremely."

This is a good start, Felicia thought happily. I'm going to make a fine critic.

After dinner, still glowing with the success of her broom-closet project, Felicia went upstairs to her room and took out an old notebook. She tore all the used pages out of it and wrote on the first clean page *Criticism Notebook.* She turned the page and wrote at the top of the next page *Constructive Criticisms.*

Then she sat with her chin in her hand, nibbling on the end of her pen, thinking. She thought for quite a while, frowning with concentration, unaware of anything but the problem she was working on.

Finally, with a satisfied sigh, she bent over her notebook and began to write.

# No Time for Talking

It was raining the next morning when Felicia came down to breakfast. The radio announcer was saying, ". . . and outside WGVM the weather is: Wet."

"Care to argue with that, Felicia?" Marilyn asked, sounding almost as if she wanted a fight.

"I haven't said anything!" Felicia cried indignantly.

"Marilyn," her mother warned, "don't start. Just don't start."

Felicia shook the cereal box. Six cornflakes fell into her bowl.

"Oh, well," she said cheerfully, going to the refrigerator. "I'd rather have a salami sandwich, anyway."

"Don't anybody say a word," Mr. Kershenbaum ordered, staring hard at Marilyn.

Marilyn popped the last of her hard-boiled egg into her mouth.

"I'm not saying a thing," she said after a few swallows. "But I don't have to sit here and watch it."

She got up and left the kitchen. Her mother sighed.

"Would you like me to drive you today?" her father asked as Felicia sliced salami and spread mustard on her sandwich.

"No, I think I'll walk."

"But Felicia, it's pouring," her mother objected.

Felicia glanced out the window. "It's not really pouring," she said. "It's more like steady drizzling."

"The weather forecast predicted rain all morning."

"Well, you know how undependable that is," Felicia said, biting into her sandwich. "I guess I can't have a soda with this. Right?"

"Don't talk with your mouth full. And no, you can't. Take some milk."

"I'm not thirsty," Felicia said.

"Maybe Marilyn wants a ride," her father said.

Felicia finished her sandwich and went to get her things together for school. On her desk were two pieces of paper, which Felicia placed carefully inside the front cover of her spelling book. She stuck her books inside a plastic zipper envelope that her father had brought from his office, making sure the spelling book was on top, where she could easily reach it when she needed her papers.

She ran downstairs and got her slicker and rain hat from the front closet. The slicker was bright red, and the hat was white with a shiny plastic finish and big red dots all over it. Felicia didn't much like the slicker, even though it was what a lot of the kids wore, because it made her hot and sticky; but she loved the hat, which had a wide brim and tied under her chin. Felicia thought she looked very nice in the hat, but that wasn't the reason she was so eager to walk to school in the rain today.

She went into the kitchen to get her lunch.

"What did you make?" she asked her mother, taking the brown paper bag from the refrigerator.

"A salami sandwich," her mother said.

"But I had that for breakfast!" Felicia exclaimed.

"Believe me, dear," her mother said, "if I had had the faintest notion that you were going to——"

"Oh, don't worry," Felicia brightened. "It really doesn't matter. I love salami." Wasn't it silly to get upset over unimportant things, when this morning was the start of Felicia's career as a constructive critic!

74

" 'Bye," she said, kissing her mother on the cheek.

" 'Bye, honey."

Felicia picked up her plastic envelope and opened the front door.

"Boots!" her mother yelled. "Felicia!"

"Rats!" Felicia sighed and hauled her boots out of the front closet. They were red rubber boots, and they didn't have heels or anything, like Phyllis's white ones, and Felicia thought they made her look dopey.

"Better luck next time," Marilyn said airily, squeezing past Felicia and out the front door.

"Are you wearing your boots?" her mother called.

"I'm wearing my stupid boots!" Felicia yelled back.

"Good-bye!"

"Good-bye," Felicia muttered and closed the front door behind her.

Her father was warming up the car in the driveway as Felicia started down the walk. "Are you sure?" he asked.

"Positive!" Felicia called back, waving her lunch at him. She was cheerful now, forgetting almost instantly about having to wear boots and concentrating on the important business ahead of her.

At the corner of Decatur Street a figure in a white trench coat and rain hat was huddled under an umbrella.

"Cheryl!" Felicia shouted happily. She'd never expected Cheryl's mother to let her walk to school in the drizzle, and Felicia clumped toward her as fast as her boots would allow.

She ducked under Cheryl's umbrella.

"My father's car wouldn't start," Cheryl explained as they started up Perry Street. "My mother wanted to call a taxi, but I wouldn't let her."

"Gee, that's great!" Felicia exclaimed. Having Cheryl along to watch her in her first public role as a constructive critic was a wonderful, unexpected surprise.

"I don't think it's so great," Cheryl said. "I don't like to walk in the rain. But I certainly wasn't going to come to school in a *taxi*."

"Listen, Cheryl," Felicia began eagerly, "I want to tell you something. When we get to——"

The honking of a horn interrupted her.

"Want a ride? Come on!" Phyllis had her head stuck out the car window. Lorraine was sitting next to her in the back seat, and Mrs. Brody was driving.

"Yes!" Cheryl yelled, struggling to close her umbrella. "Come on, Felicia."

Felicia hung back, a wave of disappointment washing over her.

She held Cheryl's arm. "No, listen, Cheryl. Let's walk. I have to——"

"Don't be stupid!" Cheryl snapped. "Why should we walk in the rain if we can get a ride?"

"It's not a rain," Felicia said desperately. "It's more like a steady drizzle——"

"Felicia, I'm getting soaked in this steady drizzle! Now, come on!"

"But Cheryl, I wanted to tell you—I have to——"

"Are you coming or aren't you?" Phyllis yelled impatiently.

"We're coming!" Cheryl called.

Felicia sighed. "All right," she agreed reluctantly. "But I'm going to get out a block before school." Cheryl didn't even hear her.

They got into the car, Felicia in the front seat next to Phyllis's mother and Cheryl in the back.

"Thanks," Cheryl said gratefully. "You're a real life-saver."

"That's a beautiful trench coat, Cheryl," Lorraine said. "Is it new?"

"Yes, my mother got it for me just last week. She said the plastic slicker was too hot and made me sweat too much."

Felicia noticed Mrs. Brody's nose twitching as if she smelled something faintly unpleasant.

"Would you let me off here, please?" Felicia said softly as they reached the corner of Perry and Homan.

"But Felicia, we're still a block from school," said Mrs. Brody, puzzled.

"Well, it's just sort of drizzling, and I really want to walk the rest of the way." She was disappointed about Cheryl, and her slicker was beginning to feel stickily uncomfortable.

All the excitement seemed to have gone out of her, leaving her feeling like an empty balloon.

Lorraine and Phyllis were admiring Cheryl's new outfit, and Cheryl wasn't even trying to get Felicia to join the conversation.

"Please," she said, putting her hand on the door handle.

"All right," Mrs. Brody said doubtfully. "If you're sure——"

"Thank you very much for the ride," said Felicia, climbing out of the car.

She trudged up the street toward school as Mrs. Brody drove on. Traffic was heavy now, with a line of cars and school buses inching up the street. On rainy days it was always like this, and very soon Felicia passed Mrs. Brody's car, stuck in traffic and not moving.

Felicia felt inside her plastic envelope for her spelling book, and her fingers groped inside the covers to feel the two pieces of paper she'd put in there. Reassuringly she kept her fingers on the papers as she approached the school crossing.

Felicia waited with a group of others for the crossing guard to wave her on. Finally he held up his hand to stop the flow of traffic and signaled to the walkers who were waiting at the curb.

They hurried across the street, heads bent against the rain, the little ones with book bags and lunch boxes banging against their knees as they trotted.

Felicia stopped in the middle of the street next to the crossing guard and drew out her papers from the spelling book.

"Move along," he said. "Let's go."

"I'd like to talk to you," Felicia began politely.

"Now? What is it?"

"I have some suggestions here——"

"Suggestions!" he roared. "Are you kidding?"

"No," Felicia said, feeling a little hurt. "Of course not. Now, I have a diagram——" Horns began honking as Felicia handed a piece of paper to the crossing guard. "You see, here is the school, and here is the——"

"Get moving!" the guard shouted. "You're holding up traffic!"

Felicia, trying to keep calm, plunged ahead with what she had to say. "Well, if you'd just look at this list of suggestions and this diagram, you'd——"

"Will you MOVE!"

Now there were cars and school buses stretching in huge lines on all sides of the crossing, and Felicia thought that every one of them must be honking its horn. The noise was nearly deafening, so Felicia practically had to scream to be heard.

"Would you at least take these and look at them?" Felicia shouted desperately, thrusting her papers into the crossing guard's hand.

He glanced at the list of suggestions. Felicia had spent almost all last evening neatly writing them out on a note pad that had "From the Desk of Felicia Kershenbaum" printed across the top.

He stuffed the list and the diagram into his raincoat pocket.

"Anything!" he shouted over the noise of the cars and the yelling of the children at the corner, who were waiting to get across the street. "Anything, if you'll just get away from here!"

"Thank you," Felicia said meekly, not even sure he could hear her. School-bus drivers were leaning out of their windows, shouting. The horns were now a steady blast, as if everybody had decided to lean on them without ever letting up. The rain had begun to come down hard, so that even Felicia had to admit it was not a drizzle anymore, but a real downpour.

The crowd of children on the corner started to cross the street without waiting for the guard to direct them. At the same time, one of the school buses maneuvered into the driveway of the school yard, even though the traffic guard had not signaled for it to go ahead; and another school bus, coming out of the driveway, came to a screeching stop just in time to keep from hitting the bus full of children.

The thought occurred to Felicia that now would be a good time to get across the street. It was going to take the crossing guard a long time to get that disaster area untangled. Felicia hoped he would read her suggestions and study her diagram. He really needed them, she thought, for he certainly was not a very efficient traffic manager.

Felicia was in art class later that morning, trying to draw how she felt.

Miss De Mara, the art teacher, had put on a record and told the pupils to draw what the music made them feel. Felicia liked Miss De Mara, but she wished that every once in a while Miss De Mara would put a bowl of fruit on her desk and say, "Draw this." Felicia could sketch pretty well if someone told her what to sketch, but thinking up something to draw was sometimes very difficult.

So Felicia sat, with pastels and charcoal on her desk, and listened to the music. It was slow and sort of sad, and it didn't actually make her feel *anything*. She drew one wavy line on her paper with a blue pastel and then drew another wavy line beneath it. She let her arm sort of sway with the rhythm of the music as she drew the lines, but that was really about all the feeling she could work up for the assignment.

"That's very good," said Miss De Mara, looking over Felicia's shoulder. "A good start. You really seem to have the flow of the music there."

"Thank you," Felicia murmured. A good start? Felicia thought she was finished. Was she supposed to do more?

"Just keep at it, class," the teacher said. "I'll be right back."

As soon as Miss De Mara was out of the room, Felicia felt a sharp poke between her shoulders. She turned around to Phyllis, who sat behind her.

"What were you doing out there this morning?" Phyllis asked.

Felicia looked at her blankly.

"This morning," repeated Phyllis impatiently. "With that crossing guard."

"Oh," Felicia said. "Oh, yeah. Just—talking." Somehow she thought it might not be a good idea to tell Phyllis exactly what she had been talking about. Felicia didn't think Phyllis would understand.

"Talking?" Phyllis echoed. "Fern and her mother were there in the car, and they said you were giving him something, and he was yelling at you. What were you talking about?"

"Oh, we were just—talking."

"Really, Felicia," Phyllis began, sounding as if she were talking to a six-year-old, "you cause the worst traffic jam in the *entire* history of the school, and you were just——"

"Me?" Felicia said indignantly. "I was just trying to——"

"All right, people," Miss De Mara said, coming back into the room, "we'll have to stop now. Assignments finished?"

But I was just trying to help, Felicia thought unhappily. I was just trying to give a little constructive criticism. A little constructive criticism never hurt anyone.

Did it?

# Sail, Calypso!

## by Adrienne Jones

*All Clay's dreams collapsed at the sight of the stranger in the boat. Clay's boat. Clay was the one who had found it, who had dug it out of the sand, and who had dreamed of making it seaworthy again.*

*Clay and Paul both claimed the right to repair the abandoned boat, but they agreed, reluctantly at first, that the job could be done more quickly if they worked together.*

*They spent the summer repairing and scraping and sanding and painting. As they worked, their friendship grew until neither of them could imagine sailing the Calypso alone.*

*Together they brought the Calypso back to life. Together they sailed the quiet waters off the shore, exploring the narrows and the channels and the small inlets. Finally they were ready to take the Calypso out to sea, out to an island some distance from shore.*

*The trip was good. The boys explored the island with enthusiasm. Then suddenly, as though the wing of some giant bird had swept above them, the sun disappeared behind a cloud, casting a dark shadow over the island. The boys thought of their return voyage to the mainland.*

"I smell rain," Clay said, rising uneasily from a rocky perch and scanning the full turn of the sky. As though to voice a threatening reply, there came the low rumble of distant thunder. The wind blew gusty and damp, cold against his body. He shivered. "C'mon!"

He turned and scrambled up over the ridge, dropping down to the leeward side, where he stopped and waited.

Paul followed without a word, eyes round and wide. Suddenly both boys felt very small in the vast world of sky and clouds and sea. When Clay spoke, it seemed the vastness swallowed his voice. The words were muffled in his own ears.

"There's the *Calypso* waiting for us."

He pointed down to where the boat lay upon the shore. Compared to the broad stretch of water between the island and the mainland, the *Calypso* seemed scarcely larger than a grain of sand.

"She's awful little, really," Paul said quietly.

In the curve of the cliffs, the air seemed still and warm. The sun shone once more. Much of the sky was hidden from view, so the blue seemed greater and the clouds of lesser importance. But the boys did not forget the way it had looked from the ridge, nor did they forget that mutter of thunder. They rushed along from ledge to ledge. Strangely, though, the downward trip seemed longer to them than had the climb upward.

"The water between the island and the mainland doesn't look so choppy," Paul spoke hopefully.

"The *Calypso*'ll take us safe," Clay said. He wished his heart was as sure as his voice sounded.

But it was true that the sea in the protected channel was marked by only an occasional whitecap, and they would be sailing before the wind, so the return trip would not take as long as that of the morning. When they finally reached the flat and ran along the sand to where the *Calypso* was beached, they were relieved that the water was still calm along the shore. The rocks and shoals would have been impossible in a heavy blow.

"C'mon, you *Calypso!*" Clay said, putting one shoulder to the bow, starting the boat out into the shallows. Paul threw his weight into the effort, and in seconds they had her afloat and had climbed aboard. Paul slipped the centerboard in place, then hurried to the bow to watch for the underwater dangers. Clay hoisted the sail, settled himself with the sheet firmly in hand, grabbed the tiller. They began to gain way.

"We'll make it just fine!" he said heartily. But even as Clay spoke the sun disappeared again, and this time the shadow held. The thunder rolled nearer than before, and the blue waters of the island turned steely gray. The *Calypso* moved uneasily through the shallows, her sail fluttering, restless in the air that moment by moment grew more gusty, more frightening.

Once Paul glanced back. He cried, "Look! Half the island's gone!" Clay looked and saw that the upper rise of the ridge was hidden in clouds.

The wind increased. Paul gripped the rails at the *Calypso*'s prow, leaning forward, anxiously scanning the gray waters that with each second deepened beneath them.

"Rocks off the starboard bow!" he cried.

Quickly Clay handled the tiller.

"Now the port side!" Paul shouted.

But presently they were past the rocks and shoals and into the deep water of the channel. The *Calypso* thrust her prow into the rising swell of the sea. Through sheet and tiller, she transmitted to Clay a kind of delight at the challenge, tunneling now through a swell, then flinging spray into the wind.

"Is this what you wanted, you dancing *Calypso* boat!" he called, shifting about, trying to hold a heading toward the mainland. They had sailed at first in an angle from the island beach in order to escape the shoals. It had been safer for that short way, sailing into the wind. But free of the threatening rocks, Clay brought the *Calypso* about, and now they were running before the wind.

They traveled more swiftly, but both boys anxiously watched the boom. The wind threatened at any moment to snatch the sail about. It had enough force to snap the mast. And without the mast . . .

Clay forced the picture from his mind, the picture of the *Calypso* helpless in the storm. He tried to fasten all his attention upon watching the sail, upon handling the tiller, upon feeling the pull of the sheet in his hand. And presently it seemed to him that he had become a part of the *Calypso,* as wise as she to the ways of wind and waves and dashing whitecaps, and as joyous as she in the challenge! And for the present the fear was gone.

When finally Paul made his way back from the prow, Clay grinned and shouted, "She'll take us back safe, Paul! Don't you worry!"

"She'd better!" Paul, catching some of Clay's spirit, laughed, and the shakiness of the sound was covered by the wind. "I don't swim very well."

Clay remembered the orange life jackets he had found so long ago, remembered he had thrust them back into the locker and forgotten them. Until now.

"Hey!" he called to Paul. "Get those orange things out of the locker. Now's when we need 'em. Just in case . . ."

So Paul found the jackets and hauled them out. He slipped into one, awkward for a moment with the two ties that fastened in front. It was bulky and clumsy and made his wide figure look like a bright orange ball.

"You'd float 'most forever in that!" Clay assured him. "Take the tiller now, and I'll get into the other one."

So finally they were both secure in their jackets, and the bright color was somehow reassuring and cheerful in the dark vastness of sea and clouds.

They could still see the mainland far ahead as the swells swept under and past them, hurrying to that low shore, now raising them to the dizzy crests, now plunging them with stomach-clutching suddenness into the troughs. There the dark swirling waters would hang above them as though to swallow the *Calypso*. But each time she lifted lightly, sweeping them clear of the fearful threat.

The rain had begun to fall. At first there were only wind-driven spits of stinging drops. Then it came more steadily. Lightning slashed across the black sky. Thunder crashed overhead. And the rain increased.

Clay struggled with tiller and sheet. Paul bailed furiously. The water from the downpour mixed with the seawater that the *Calypso* had already shipped. Slowly the water rose until it was as high as the boys' ankles, a small sea of itself, dashing and sloshing about as the boat pitched and tossed in the running swells.

The boys worked to keep the *Calypso* more or less free of water and on the proper heading, and there was no time for fear. Once Paul stopped bailing to peer forward through the overcast and the sheeting rain.

"I can't see land anymore!" he yelled.

"Me neither!" And for only a second Clay took his eyes from the mast and the danger of the swinging boom. "I'm trying to keep the wind behind us! And the swells are running toward the beach! Maybe we ought to try to take the sail in. The water's bound to push us in to shore!"

He didn't like to think of the size of the breakers that would be pounding the beach. How would they ever get the *Calypso* in with the waves breaking over the stern! But there was no time to worry about that.

"Shall I lower the sail?" Paul called.

"Yeah. Be careful! Don't go overboard! You'd never get back in! Not the way the *Calypso*'s rolling!"

Paul stowed the bailing can. He moved cautiously forward, gripping the rail. He reached for the mast, stretching to keep to the safety of the rail until he had grasped the spar with one hand. Then, wary of the boom, he pulled himself over, crouched low, and with a tight hold on the mast, began to work with the halyard. It was wet, and his fingers were icy. With the wind behind them, the sail jerked and bucked and pulled so tight that he could not manage the soaked line.

The light had turned to a leaden dusk. The island and the mainland had long since disappeared. But the *Calypso*, even with the water she had shipped, was still buoyant, steadfastly plunging along.

Clay close-hauled the sheet, as much as his strength would allow. The boom wrenched at the hard twist of rope, and it bit into his fingers, leaving them raw in the salty spray. He knew now they should have lowered the sail long ago. Anxiously he glanced at Paul who still clung to the mast, trying to loosen the jammed halyard. Once Paul turned, and Clay could see him shake his head, but once again Paul bent doggedly to the task. He hunched against the rain and the cold gray water that raked over the *Calypso*'s bow each time the boat climbed a swell or slipped down into the next trough. And all the while he kept his body pressed to the mast, his arms encircling the spar as he worked. Clay clung to the biting sheet and steadied the tiller, peering through the blackness that pressed around them, smothering his fear.

"Man, if those clouds would only rise up a little," he muttered to himself, to the *Calypso*. "If I was just sure we're sailing for the beach instead of China . . ."

Then presently, as though the clouds had plucked his wish from the swirling air, they lifted a little above the water's surface and thinned a bit.

Clay was sorry he had uttered the words!

For before the clouds closed in once more, the *Calypso* had topped a white-ridged swell, and Clay had his view of the mainland. It was nearer, much nearer, than he had thought it would be! Even from this seaward side he could see the breakers pounding the beach, making a foaming terror of the surf. In that brief view before the clouds closed in once more, the boiling stretch of sea looked like certain death for the *Calypso*.

"Paul!" Clay shouted. "Paul——"

The other did not hear him, but seemed glued to the mast as though intending to work through eternity at the task of the jammed line.

Desperately Clay screamed, "Paul! Paul! We gotta turn! Watch the boom! We gotta turn! Paul! Watch out——"

Though the wind seemed to smother his cry before it left his lips, it could not mask another sound—the wild clash of the surf along the shore; the thundering, pounding force that would break the *Calypso* into a thousand pieces and that would grind Paul and himself into the sand along the ocean floor.

Once more he screamed, "Paul!"

As though Clay's desperation reached the other when the sound could not, Paul raised his head and looked back.

"I'm gonna come around!" Clay shouted. "Keep your head down! Hold on!"

Now Paul shrank against the mast, holding tightly, watching Clay struggle with the yanking sheet. His blue eyes were wide, but he seemed calm enough and even managed an encouraging nod, though by now he could hear the roar of the surf and understood the danger. Their eyes held for an instant, then Clay was putting the tiller over just as the *Calypso* started to slide down the steep backslope into a trough.

The sturdy craft managed half the turn before hitting the bottom of the trough. The dark water seemed to pile above her on all sides. Clay forced the tiller as far as it would go. Just as the bow began to finish the arc of its turn, the rising slope of the next wave began to lift her. All might have gone well, but a vicious lash of wind caught the sail from the new angle, yanked it against the *Calypso*'s natural roll. She plunged to one side. The starboard rail raked beneath the water. Clay was thrown to the bottom of the boat. In that instant he lost his hold on the tiller, and the sheet whipped free, lashing this way and that.

He floundered, helpless, in the sloshing water that the *Calypso* had shipped. He clung to one bench, pulled himself about facing the stern, almost reached the tiller, then slipped again. He felt the boom scrape the top of his head. He ducked low as he struggled to regain his footing. The plunging of the boat now whirled him about again, and he had a glimpse of Paul. The other had let go his hold on the mast and was clutching the rail, trying to work himself back to help his friend.

"Watch out for the boom!" Clay shouted, but again he floundered in the shipped water. This time he fell against the bench, cutting his cheek. Blood spread down the wet dark skin along his jaw.

"Clay!" Paul cried. And then forgetting the danger of the boom, he half stood, reaching to help the other.

"Look out! Paul!" Clay shouted, unaware of his own hurt.

But the vicious swipe of the boom caught Paul along the side of his head. He slumped across the rail, a limp bright orange pillow. As Clay watched in horror, unable to help, Paul teetered there, then slowly rolled over, disappeared from sight.

# One Last Glimpse

Fear for his friend lifted Clay from the boat's floor. Flinging himself at the tiller, he managed to head the *Calypso* shoreward, directly into the rolling swells. All the while he scanned the waters for the bright life jacket. Twice he glimpsed it off the *Calypso's* port rail. At first it was close to the boat. Then the gap widened, and Paul appeared to be facedown, though it was difficult to see in the gloom. Frantically Clay secured the sheet so the sail was set at a proper angle for sailing into the wind. He lashed the tiller in place with a quick turn of line to try and keep the *Calypso* heading straight seaward. Maybe he'd have a chance of bringing Paul back to the boat. Maybe—if the surge of the sea offset the *Calypso's* effort to make way—she might stay almost in the same place. Maybe——

Awkward in the bulky jacket, he worked his way along the rail. He kept looking for Paul in the roll of black water. The orange blob had disappeared. Wary of the boom, he reached the mast. Clinging to the spar, he stepped on the bench. Balanced there. Searching. Searching.

*Paul.*

Clay swallowed at the panic in his throat.

*Paul.*

And strangely he remembered how Paul had looked that first day. He remembered Paul peering over the rail of the little abandoned boat. Just like an owl. A pale owl. He had hated the Owl for being on the *Calypso*. For claiming any right to the *Calypso*. When had the friendship truly begun? He couldn't remember! Now it was not the *Calypso's* fate that caused the sick feeling in his middle.

*Paul!*

The *Calypso* climbed up the next long slope. As she rose the view broadened.

"Paul!" Clay cried, filled with terror.

There! There, a splash of orange! Closer than Clay could possibly have hoped!

And Paul was not facedown. Instead, he floundered dizzily. He seemed unable to keep his head clear of the water for more than a few seconds at a time. He'd never make it to shore!

"Paul! Hold on—" Clay screamed.

With all his strength he thrust himself away from the mast, kicked with all the power of his sturdy legs, and leaped from the rail. Then he was in the water, striking out for the spot he had fixed upon.

His life jacket made swimming difficult; but each time the white-topped swells thrust him under, the buoyant jacket popped him back to the surface again. The water was cold and punishing. But on he swam, thrusting steadily with arms and legs, heedless of the fact that he was under the water as often as on top. He held his breath when he had to, gasped for air when he could. He caught no glimpse of Paul. To find him would be a miracle!

His desperation edged again toward panic. If he couldn't find Paul soon, it would be too late! Then just as he was sure the search had failed, he saw a flash of orange. The bright color had shown just at the crest of the swell ahead. He himself floundered in the trough. Now he strained to keep his head clear of the water. Up he rose on the rush of the next wave.

There it was again—the orange jacket! Catching the forward thrust of the swell just below its crest, Clay swam with all his strength. The orange jacket had settled in the trough and now it began to rise. Furiously Clay pumped with arms and legs, managing to ride just in front of the white crest. He could see Paul's face now, his mouth struggling for breath, his eyes nearly closed against the stinging spray. The water slapped into his open mouth time after time, and his arms, thrusting from the jacket, thrashed feebly.

Just as a huge wave overtook him, Clay gave one last thrust, touched the orange jacket with outstretched fingers, lost it, and started down the back of the swell. Over the crest came the jacket, the gasping mouth, the weakly struggling arms. Once more Clay thrust forward, snatched at the orange blob. Had it! Shifted his grasp! Now his grip was firm! He slipped one hand under Paul's chin, cupping his fingers over the open mouth, protecting it from the churning salt water.

"You're all right!" Clay managed to say close to his friend's ear. "Take it easy, you old Paul."

He was gasping himself from the effort of the swim. For the first time he was grateful for the awkward life jacket. Now it kept him afloat and helped to save his strength. He supported Paul, keeping his head as far out of the water as he could, speaking whenever possible to reassure him.

"Go ahead—Breathe—I got you—That's it—See, we're okay—Breathe again—The jackets make us safe—safe as a bathtub—Breathe—That's it——"

It must have been the blow from the boom that had made Paul so helpless, for now, slowly, he began to recover a little. Finally he was able to breathe when he should, hold his breath when the water swept over them.

But Clay kept his grip on the other's jacket. Now he re-membered the *Calypso.* Their little *Calypso!* Where was she? Was there any hope they could reach her?

Just as he was thinking that she must already have gone down or maybe was dashing to pieces on the beach, he saw her.

"Hey—" he cried. "Over there, she's sailing——"

Weakly, Paul twisted his head, but when the wind-driven water slashed into his face, he turned away.

"She's sailing straight out to sea—" Clay gasped, straining to see, blinking the stinging spray from his eyes. "She's leaving us!"

When Clay glanced again at the *Calypso,* he saw that the distance between them had widened. He had secured the sheet and lashed the tiller, and the little boat had picked up the westerly. It was as though her own spirit had taken command. She had managed to free herself of the shoreward-sweeping currents. She was heeling over to leeward, racing gaily across her sea, heading straight away from the land that had too long held her captive. She would not die upon the shore!

"The surf—" Clay heard Paul's voice.

He wrenched his gaze from the flying *Calypso.* At this moment they rode high on the crest of a mountain of dark water. The sea had swept them closer to shore. There was the beach, no more than two hundred yards away. But the surf! They had one terrible view of it before they dropped down the back of the swell.

"Next swell's gonna put us in it!" cried Clay.

Now from the trough the water rushed them upward again. It seemed as though this time they shot straight to the sky. They both gasped. For only an instant they looked down on all that surrounded them. The roar and thunder of tons of water crashed on the flat shore. Clay saw that the crest they rode was passing beneath them. He knew it would drop them for the next huge wave to bury. He glanced back. The sea was gathering itself, rising behind them.

But beyond the piling water he caught a last brief glimpse of the *Calypso*. She was growing small with the distance. She still flew straight away to sea. Her sail stretched tight in the gale. Her blue hull gleamed clean and bold.

"Hey, sail, you *Calypso*—" he shouted, but his voice was lost.

The swell dropped them in the trough. The wave behind piled higher. Rising. Rising. Up. Up. Now the crest seemed to climb upon itself, curving high above them. Suddenly they felt themselves sucked upward. For an instant as they swept up the smooth wall of water, they saw they were inside a curving liquid tunnel.

Together they yelled! Then they were whirled up and over into the foaming top. From there it crashed them down with its own tons of salty water. Down, down. Tumbling. Whirling. They were swept for what seemed like an eternity along the sand of the bottom. At last they shot to the surface. But they had become separated.

Clay gagged, with the salt water choking him. Then he managed a gasp of air. There was churning foam all around, and before he could truly catch his breath, he was snatched up into another giant, curving wave. Thrown to the bottom. Then up to the top. Gasping, choking. A little air for the lungs. Then up and over and down again. And again. And again, until he was sure each next one would truly finish him. The nightmare of the whirling sea was endless.

One particular thrust of water, more vicious than the rest, crashed him against the sand with such force that he blacked out for a moment. Then he gradually became aware that he lay on his back, looking up from the pale depths as

the water sheeted away, slipping back to the sea. Now he found he could breathe air instead of having to swallow salt water. With tremendous effort he turned over, found himself on his hands and knees in the thin surf of the shore. Before he could struggle to his feet another wave rushed upon him. But it was gone in a moment, and Clay found himself standing, staggering, slipping, falling, standing again, staggering up the flat of the beach. There he collapsed.

He thought of Paul, but he could not move. He felt himself gag, and salt water poured from his mouth and his nose. He began to shiver, but he still could not force himself to rise.

"Are you all right, Clay?"

The voice was close to him, and he felt a hand on his shoulder. He nodded weakly. Finally he rolled over, sat up. There was Paul crouching beside him, his round eyes full of concern.

"It looks like your head got banged in the surf. There's a big bump here." Clay could feel Paul touch the side of his head. He remembered that last crashing wave that had slammed him into the sand. "You'll feel better in a while, Clay. I guess you just about swallowed the whole ocean." Then after a bit, "You're shaking all over. You wait. I'll be back in a few minutes."

Too weak to protest, Clay put his head down on his arms and let the shivering have its way. The rain had lessened, and he was vaguely aware that the light was brighter than it had been. Presently the rain stopped altogether, but the wind blew cold upon his wet body. Time seemed of no importance, and only vaguely he wondered where Paul had gone.

"Keep that around you. I'll start a fire."

It was Paul, and he had placed something dry and protecting across Clay's back.

After a bit Clay stopped his shivering and the sick feeling in his middle began to ease. He raised his head and looked around. It wasn't raining and he saw that the clouds to the west were beginning to thin. To the south there were a few streaks of pale blue showing. The ocean remained cold and gray, and the waves still pounded the shore. But the island was free of the overcast. There it stood, out toward the horizon, and it seemed impossible that they had sailed there and landed on that far, strange shore.

There was not a sign of the *Calypso*. She was gone. Back to her beloved sea.

# There the Grass Grows Soft

# Showdown on the Tundra

by Ron Rau

The day it happened I had decided to take a walk after working the night shift. Work was on the north slope of the Brooks Range in Alaska. It was May 1974, and construction of the trans-Alaska pipeline had begun. I had taken a job at the northernmost camp in the mountains.

Directly to the south of camp, the mountains looked like upside-down V's—steep and rugged. To the east and west, about three miles away, the mountains were not so fierce-looking; they were even rounded a little on top. To the north were the rolling hills that gently sloped down to the Arctic Ocean more than a hundred miles away. I decided to walk north with my camera so I could get a picture of the camp with the rugged mountains to the south as a background.

It was four in the morning when I started walking. Already there was enough light for a good picture, the Arctic summer being upon us. To the east, the sun was hidden behind the mountains, casting a magnificent glow on the highest peaks to the south and west. That was the picture I wanted.

I had been walking about fifteen minutes when I came across a caribou antler three feet long and bleached white by the sun. It would make a perfect addition to the picture. I could lay it on a knoll and frame the camp inside the curved antler. It had six sharp tines, two of which were broken.

Carrying the antler, I walked for another hour toward the hill where I wanted to take the picture.

Then I saw the wolf, barely fifty yards away. It was coming into my path at an angle with that peculiar bouncing walk that wolves have.

I stopped.

The wolf walked—walked is the wrong word—it bounced along on little springs set into its knees until it was directly in front of me. Then it turned and looked at me as though it had known all along that I was there.

My first response was to look for other wolves. The tundra was treeless and rolling, well gullied and knolled. This is why I had not seen the wolf earlier; it had probably just come out of a gully.

There it stood, on those tremendously long legs, staring at me. The nearest tree was at least a hundred miles away, but still I thought about it. Since guns are not allowed in the construction camp, all I had to protect myself were the caribou antler and a jackknife.

Wolves seldom, if ever, attack, I said to myself.

I knew this to be true, but there stood an animal fifty yards away, hackles raised, staring at me—an animal that could kill me. Did it know that?

I knew that I could not show fear. In some peculiar way, animals can sense fear. If this wolf sensed my fear . . . well, I could be in trouble. Maybe I was anyway.

I stood motionless.

I can't say how long we looked at each other. Ten seconds, thirty, a minute maybe. I thought. Hard. Fast. There was no place to run. There was no place to hide. I was two miles from camp and the safety of the buildings and my companions. Obviously, I had no choice in the matter. There was only one response I could make. I must convince the wolf that I was not a creature to be fooled with.

I decided to take my chances with the caribou antler. It was heavy enough and stout, and the tines were six to eight inches long. If it came to a showdown, I would go for the wolf's ribs, hoping that a tine would penetrate between them into the lungs. I would have my jackknife opened in my left hand.

Suddenly the wolf began to circle.

I forgot about the knife.

I began walking toward camp, directly in line with the wolf.

It stopped. I stopped.

Then I noticed the wind. Perhaps the wolf would smell me and be scared away. Any other wild animal, except perhaps the grizzly bear—and even most of them—would have run. Obviously, this wolf was not afraid of me. I began to realize what a dangerous position I was in. I had taken a lot for granted—namely, my safety.

The wolf started circling again. I started walking.

It stopped. I stopped.

We studied each other. The wolf was grayish-yellow and weighed about eighty pounds. Half my weight. Even so, it could kill me. How helpless human beings are, I thought, unable to hold their own against animals half their size. And what a magnificent creature this animal seemed to be. Its long, powerful legs were perfectly developed for running in the tundra. Running was the name of the game out here.

Again the wolf began circling. I began walking. Now I had a clear shot at camp . . . two miles away. There was no way I could outrun the wolf, but I felt a little better not having it directly between me and camp. That was a false feeling of security, I knew, but still it was comforting.

I forced my mind off camp and back to the caribou antler, which was my real security. Go for the ribs, I told myself. I kept looking at the tines. If only I had time to sharpen them on a rock! Then I would have something that might penetrate the wolf's thick hide.

The wolf stopped. I stopped.

It sat down, facing me.

I longed to know what it was going to do. Why had it sat down? Surely it wasn't afraid. Or was it?

I decided to make the next move. Toward camp. The wolf was on my left, far off the line to camp, but still only fifty yards away. It had been circling carefully, getting neither closer nor farther away.

I took a step, and the wolf leaped to its feet as though stung by a bee. I stopped, frozen in my tracks. It circled, and I began walking again.

Wolves seldom, if ever, attack, I told myself.

But they're supposed to run, another voice said.

The wolf stopped. I stopped.

It was facing me, and I could clearly see its raised hackles. I growled, not instinctively, but a well-thought-out growl. Again I considered using the caribou antler. It was a little long for a quick swing, a little burdensome for hand-to-hand combat. No. Hand-to-teeth combat. Go for the ribs.

The wolf moved again. Directly toward me.

I moved toward the wolf, growling, this time a little more instinctively.

We moved a dozen steps toward each other before the wolf stopped.

I stopped.

Five seconds passed. I knew what I had to do. I had to make the next move.

I stepped forward and the wolf leaped six feet to one side as though stung again. Then it retreated those dozen

steps it had taken earlier. Back at least fifty yards to where it had been circling. It stopped and looked at me.

I stopped. My whole body swelled with relief. The wolf had retreated. It had shown fear! Or at least the closest thing to fear—confusion. For the first time I realized that I was shaking. But it was over, wasn't it? The wolf had retreated. It didn't want a fight.

I turned away and began walking toward camp. The animal was off to the side circling again. I speeded up.

Don't walk too fast, I shouted inside my brain. The wolf might sense fear. So I stopped and faced it again. It stopped.

We were now about seventy-five yards apart, too far for me to see if its hackles were still raised. We stared at each other for at least a minute, and I then turned and began walking again.

This time I did not stop. If the wolf followed, I knew what I was going to do. I should have done it in the first place. I would stop and tie my jackknife to the end of the antler. I could use a bootlace. Perhaps I should stop and do it now, I thought. No, keep walking. The wolf was following me, sniffing my tracks and raising its nose to the wind. Then it went into a gully and disappeared from sight.

Five minutes passed. No wolf! I walked rapidly, straight for the construction camp. It seemed a lot closer now. Fifteen minutes passed. Still no wolf. For the first time I felt safe. What an incredible relief. I found that I had developed a very warm feeling for my bleached caribou antler. Without it, I might have acted differently. I might not have had the nerve to walk toward the wolf with only a jackknife.

I wondered what the wolf had in mind when it came toward me. What would have happened if I had walked toward camp instead of toward the wolf? What would have happened if I had panicked and run? What would I have done without the antler? There was no way of knowing, because my whole defense had been dependent on the antler.

Soon I was standing on a knoll three hundred yards from camp. I could smell bacon. The day shift had just got up and was going to breakfast. The sun had cleared the mountain to the east. It was an incredible morning.

I stood on the knoll, wondering what to do with the antler. I could take it with me, but it would cheapen the value of the antler to take it away. It had served me well. I could always have it anyway, in my mind. This is where it belongs, I thought.

I let it fall to the ground. It broke in half.

# In Tune with Our Timber Wolves

by Dave Mech and John Winship

It was a cold December day in 1969 when Jack Meier, driving along lonely Highway 1, spotted the timber wolf wading up a snowy embankment toward the road. Jack stopped the car. He slid carefully out the door, uncased his gun, and loaded it. After all, it wasn't every day that a trapper had a chance to nail a wolf at point-blank range.

Jack Meier had nothing in particular against wolves. In fact, he kind of liked them. Or at least he admired and respected them. But he was a logger and a trapper, making his living from the woods. And in his part of the country it was standard practice to pot a wolf whenever possible. Besides, there were no laws to keep him from doing so.

It was just second nature for Jack to take advantage of this golden opportunity—a wolf standing well within range during broad daylight.

Then suddenly Jack saw the collar. Right away he knew what it was. This animal was "1051," a radio-tagged wolf whose whereabouts were being watched almost daily. In fact, this was the first wolf to be radio-tracked in Minnesota. Jack was not about to interfere with the tracking project, even though he was perfectly within his legal rights to shoot the wolf.

It wasn't long after Jack had put away his gun and the wolf had bounded off toward a swamp that a red and white ski-plane began circling over the swamp. The ski-plane, a U.S. Fish and Wildlife Service plane, proved to Jack that he had been right. The wolf *had* been radio-tagged!

Almost daily Jack had seen this aircraft come in high from faraway. He had watched it descend and circle over parts of the Superior National Forest. He knew that a directional antenna, mounted on each wing, could pick up a wolf's radio signal from 20 miles away and follow it right back to the wolf. Now the airplane was homing in on 1051.

Inside the aircraft we knew nothing about the wolf's close call. We had just followed our standard routine of finding the wolf, watching it, and then flying off to follow another signal. Not until a few days later did we learn that Jack had almost shot *our* wolf.

"It's a good thing you guys came over the other day and told me what you're up to," he said. It certainly was.

Less than a week before, we had alerted Jack Meier and the other trappers in the area that 1051 had come 17 miles south into their country. We had explained our research program and asked them not to shoot or trap our wolf if they could help it. They understood and seemed to be almost as eager as we were to find out just where this wolf would go.

During the next week, 1051 hung around Jack Meier's area, covering some 45 square miles. Then on January 5 it headed back north and stayed within an area of about 13 square miles. A carful of loggers caught it out on a woods road and "bumped" it a few times with their fender. However, it managed to escape unharmed.

After another month, 1051 left that area and settled into one of about 16 square miles, some 11 miles to the northwest. Three weeks later, it crossed into Canada for a day or so. Then it suddenly started a south-southwest trek that was to last for at least two months.

During most of 1051's journey, we made weekly tracking trips. On each flight we found the wolf in some new and surprising area: Isabella, Two Harbors, Wales, Canyon, Central Lakes, Floodwood, and finally the Grand Rapids area. On April 24 at 3:30 p.m. we saw 1051 for the last time. It was heading northwest toward Grand Rapids. We never heard from our wolf again.

Whether the transmitter faded out or the wolf slipped out of our range during the next week we will never know. Perhaps it was killed and its collar was broken open, thus shutting off the radio. In any case, we were most pleased to have tracked 1051 as far as we did.

The straight-line distance between its most northerly and most southerly location measured 129 miles. But the actual distance the wolf covered during this two-month trek was probably at least 500 miles.

Every time we go over the data and maps from this tracking project, we thank Jack Meier for not pulling the trigger when he had such a good opportunity to do so.

The timber wolf is listed among the endangered species of the world, and research programs are underway to

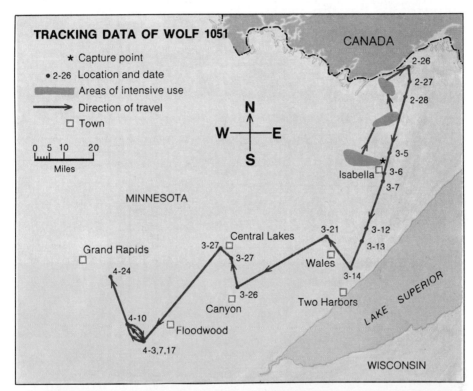

obtain information about its habits. In addition, studies are being made to discover the number of wolves that live in a given area. Counting wolves is not easy. This is especially true in Minnesota, where the wolf population is large. Also, the wolf range covers thousands of square miles. In fact, the wolf population of Minnesota does not appear to be threatened. Even so, research programs are needed. Such programs depend on radio-tracking techniques.

Wolves are trapped, ear-tagged, weighed, and outfitted with radio-collars. The radios transmit for several months. Some may last for more than a year. Throughout most seasons the radio-tagged wolves are tracked by airplanes once a week. During the breeding season, they are tracked almost daily.

Of course, in the process of counting and following the movements of wolves, it is possible to obtain other

important data as well. Their breeding habits, denning habits, activity patterns, and the history of the young in the pack are recorded.

There is so little known about timber wolves, and there has been so much misinformation passed around about them, that it is most encouraging to have a good technique for obtaining solid facts. The full success of the program, however, depends on the least amount of human interference and the greatest amount of human help.

Hunter, spare that wolf!

# That Quail, Robert

by Margaret A. Stanger

Until July 11, 1962, we had no hint of the change about to take place in our lives. On that date there was no Robert; there was just an abandoned egg in a deserted wet nest. We had known that a quail was nesting in the deep grass beyond the rose garden. My friend and neighbor, Dr. Thomas Kienzle, had discovered the nest in June, and he had carefully left the surrounding grass uncut.

By patient observation and long periods of standing motionless, he had seen the little hen go to the nest. He had watched as she reached out with her bill, covering herself with the grasses around her—from one side, from the other side, from front and back, until she was completely hidden. She had chosen her spot well.

Tommy and Mildred Kienzle had built their house high on a bank above a lake, and since it was surrounded by woods, it was a haven for wildlife. As he cleared lawns and paths, Tommy had purposely left piles of brush in among the trees, because quail had often been seen around the place. Of course he had no idea as to when the eggs would hatch, but both he and Mildred were on the alert for them.

On that eventful July morning, Tommy went to get the car for a trip into town. As he neared the garage, which is some distance from the house, he was aware of movement in the grass, and his attention was immediately drawn to a female quail apparently in distress. She was in the middle of the driveway, dragging one wing as though it were broken, and seeming to struggle. Tommy stood very still and then saw the male bird, going through a similar performance. He realized immediately that he was witnessing a most remarkable act of parental courage. The parents were definitely drawing his attention to themselves, away from their young. As he stood quietly, he saw two or three tiny balls of fluff moving off the driveway to safety, evidently obeying some kind of direction from the mother. Tommy moved softly back toward the house and was rewarded by seeing twelve young quail led into the woods. In a few minutes he got the car, picked up Mildred, and recounted what he had just been privileged to see. As they drove out of the yard, he said, "Look! There they are! The mother quail and—two, four, eight—there are twelve of them, just going past the rosebush toward the pine trees."

He and Mildred sat quietly in the car as the mother quail led the little balls of brown fluff off to safety. Because of their coloring, it was hard to follow them even a short distance.

"I've read that the quail hen never returns to the place where the chicks were hatched, so when we come home we will have a look at the nest," said Mildred as they drove down the driveway. But before they returned, there was a thunderstorm, and they did not visit the nest until the next morning. Even though they knew almost exactly where to look, it was cleverly hidden and not easy to find. They stood looking at it—just a little cup-shaped hollow in among the grass.

"Wait a minute," said Tommy. "I think there is something in it." Sure enough, down in the mud were two eggs, one badly cracked and one perfect. He picked up the perfect one. It was very dirty and covered with tiny, lively mites. They took it into the house, washed it with cold water, sprayed it with bug spray, and left it on the kitchen counter as a curiosity. Later in the day they noticed a small crack in the shell, so just in case, they put a small lamp beside it for warmth.

For two days they watched it. Nothing happened. But on the third day they thought the egg moved slightly. As they held it to their ears, they could hear a faint ticking inside.

A quail egg is a lovely thing. It is snowy white, about an inch long, softly rounded at one end and fairly pointed at the other. There certainly was something going on in this one. As they stood watching, tiny holes began to appear around the pointed end. When there was an almost complete circle of holes, a slight trembling came

from within, and the shell parted. There emerged slowly something resembling a wet bumblebee in size and general appearance. It lay there apparently exhausted, and Tommy and Mildred stood watching it in amazement. The living room clock interrupted the silence by striking two, and Mildred realized in horror that they had completely forgotten lunch.

The tiny thing was drying off, moment by moment, and before they went in to eat, they moved the lamp and the chick to the corner of the counter. They barricaded it with cereal boxes and a bag of groceries, more to keep it warm and protected than for any other reason.

When halfway through the meal, they heard a little chirp, and there in the doorway stood the baby, the body now fluffed to the size of an English walnut, tottering unsteadily on its tiny legs. They rushed to pick it up, realizing that it must have fallen off the edge of the counter to the floor. A small space between a cereal box and the bag showed clearly where the bird had found its way out of the barricade. Even at the age of about an hour, it had followed the sound of human voices and found the first living creatures it was to encounter—two human beings.

Greatly concerned lest the fall had injured the baby, Tommy and Mildred feared this might be the end of the story—but it wasn't. It was just the beginning. Evidently more security must be provided, so a carton was found and bird, lamp, and all were placed inside. The tiny bird looked pitiful and miserably alone. Suddenly Mildred remembered a small lamb's-wool duster, which she put in the corner of the box, tying it so that the wooly part was an inch or so above the bottom of the box. That looked better. Bobby White, as he was immediately called, seemed to like it too, and was under it almost as soon as it was in place. Within half an hour from the time he was hatched, the baby had begun to change in appearance. He was now brown instead of black, and grew fluffier and downier by the minute.

What to do now was the question. Mildred called a friend who was interested in birds, and received no encouragement at all as to the best way to save Bobby's life. However, the friend suggested that they go to the local duck farm and get some baby-chick starter, which they immediately did. A jar lid full of chick starter, another containing water, and they were in business. The baby, while seeming to like the duster from the beginning, paid no attention to the food and water. For eight hours he did not eat at all. Many people, hearing the tale, have thought that he was force-fed at first. Not so. The only help he had was when his tiny bill was gently dipped in the water. From then on—no help.

As I attempt to relate this extraordinary tale, I am grateful that I have been privileged to watch this tiny bird as he grew and developed. I did not see him until the second morning of his life, when I was taken into the kitchen and invited to look in the carton. I saw the lamp, the duster, and the lids of food and water, but nothing else. Mildred gently picked up the duster, and there snuggled inside it was the exquisite little bird.

She picked him out from the nest of wool, and he ate his breakfast with enthusiasm. I felt strongly that he should have a more deserving name than Bobby, and I immediately called him Robert; and Robert he has been to all of us since then. Even then, at the puffball stage, he was really beautiful, with soft shadings in his coloring, lighter on the breast than on the back. He had very bright little eyes.

The lamb's-wool duster proved to have been a real inspiration. Had Robert stayed with his quail mother, he would have snuggled in similar comfort, because the under-feathers of the adult quail are so soft that they resemble fur or wool.

I wonder why it is that people are so outspokenly gloomy about a little wild creature's chances for survival. At this stage the prediction of the neighborhood was, "He'll never live." Then, after he had survived and thrived for several days, there were such comments as: "You'll never be allowed to keep him" . . . "It's against the law to keep a wild bird" . . . "You'll be in trouble," and so on and on.

The doctor and Mildred had very firm answers: "We aren't going to cage this little thing. We aren't even handling him any more than we have to, just to clean the carton and keep him warm and fed. He will be freed outdoors as soon as he is strong enough, but we can't put him out in the big world now. He wouldn't stand a ghost of a chance if we did."

It turned out that only Robert himself knew the answers to the doubters. In the first place, time was to prove that he had no intention of leaving his new home for the unknown. And we were to learn that our idea that he might be taken back into his own family of brothers and sisters was impossible. Quail will not accept any bird who has been in contact with human beings.

Robert's development was outstanding in three areas: communication, plumage, and personality. From the second day, he greeted his providers with definite chirps of pleasure. We could tell without looking in the carton what was going on—the happy busy chirps were made while he was eating, the little sad coos meant he wanted companionship, and the soft trills, more throaty purr than birdcall, told us he was drowsy.

He was never nervous, and he adjusted to his surroundings immediately. We could look in at him as he cuddled under the duster or we would work around in the kitchen without disturbing him. When he uttered his trills, it was hard to believe that he was a quail and not a lovebird. There was a large cage of lovebirds at the far end of the kitchen, and I often wondered if it could be possible that he imitated them. We shall never know, but the trills continued.

Robert skipped the homely pinfeathery stage common to many chicks. His chest was the first to give indication of its later beauty as the soft feathers appeared over the down in a chain-mail pattern. Each little beige feather had a lighter spot toward the tip, the tip itself being a fine border of very dark brown. The end result was exquisite.

The top of his head darkened soon, with tiny lines of an almost old-gold color down the sides, which set off his eyes startlingly. We had supposed the eyes to be black, but they were dark brown with coal-black pupils. Around the base of his neck appeared a band of light brown, which darkened at the lower edge and in front melted into the general pattern of the breast. Tiny softly patterned feathers covered his back, and the last to appear were the long wing and tail feathers. Each feather, with the exception of those forming wing and tail, was double, with the other feather having a separate underfeather of down coming from the same shaft. Even the tiniest ones were double. By the time Robert was a few weeks old, he was a beautiful little quail, although he did not achieve the full measure of his magnificent coloring and feathering until the age of three months.

The most incredible part of his development was the emerging personality. At the age of two weeks, he showed a real fondness for the doctor, often going to sleep in his hands while the carton was being cleaned. This was a clear indication that the time had come to let him free. The summing up of the discussion was: "We have to do it sometime. We just have to make up our minds to that."

On a warm, sunny day in early August when Robert was three weeks old, they carried him out of the house and set him on the lawn. The reaction was unexpected. He looked around in bewilderment for a minute or two, then with excited little calls he began scratching and biting off tender tips of grass. Almost immediately he encountered a tiny bug, which he ran after and ate.

Mildred and Tommy stayed out with him for about an hour, during which time Robert was busy and very contented. They felt that he knew instinctively how to find food, and they walked toward the house. They reached the front door and Tommy was putting his finger on the latch when a sharp, piercing call came from Robert

several yards behind them, a call that said, "Hey! Wait for me!" As the door opened, Robert came running as fast as his legs could carry him, and he darted into the house ahead of them. After this performance had been repeated for many days, the answer was evident: Robert was not going to leave. From then on, he was out-of-doors a great deal, staying near Tommy while he weeded flower beds or raked the lawn. Robert had come to stay.

From the moment Robert first refused the invitation to return to the wild and ran back into the doorway, the house was his. His adjustment to its size was quite remarkable. With neck outstretched and head tipped slightly to one side, he stalked around investigating everything. An early discovery was that sometimes a tiny spider could be found in the baseboard. For weeks, on being taken out of his carton in the morning, Robert would make the rounds investigating the baseboards. The house was large and new, and for some time those little spiders had been a real nuisance. Within a few weeks Robert accomplished the seemingly impossible feat of completely ridding the place of the spiders.

One of the surprises accompanying his becoming a regular member of the household was his marked liking for companionship. Where the family members were, there, too, was Robert. If Mildred was sewing in the sewing room, Robert was there, investigating patterns, running off with bits of cloth, and generally busying himself with the project. If Tommy was reading the news-paper, Robert was in his lap, begging for attention. When he found that Tommy's interest was really on the paper, he would give up to the point of nestling in the crook of Tommy's arm or on his shoulder.

Robert was two months old on September 14, and we celebrated by having tea out on the Kienzles' patio. Robert had a cupcake topped with two small candles. The plate on which it was served was covered with fresh chickweed, the stems anchored by the cake. They were not anchored long. Every bit of the chickweed disappeared in a few minutes, and then he ate all the cake he could hold. We smile now to think what an important date that seemed. Later we celebrated only actual birthdays.

# Well Done, Robert

Spring approached, and with it came a little gnawing fear in the hearts of Robert's human friends. Robert had come through the winter in fine spirits, if not in fine feather. Although he'd had little outdoor exercise and almost no really good dirt baths, he was as chipper and sweet as ever. With spring came the molting season. Feathers were everywhere, first the little double-shafted breast and back feathers, and then more and more often a large wing feather. How a little bird of Robert's size could shed enough feathers to fill a shoe box is a mystery. But he did. For a time he had only one rather ratty tail feather; but to our eyes he was still a delight. In fact, Robert was an inspiration to everyone.

The gnawing fear concerned all that was happening. Would Robert respond to the call of the season and the mating instinct? We had long agreed that some change was bound to happen, and if it should take this form, we would accept it as best for Robert. The adult quail began appearing in pairs, and we knew the season was upon us. As the weather permitted more time for him to be out-side, we kept a careful watch—just in case. But so far, he did not seem interested.

With the molting season, we had expected his behavior to change along with his plumage; we were prepared for him to be listless and moody. However, this did not happen. Weeks of feather-dropping went by and Robert remained as gay as a cricket. We began thinking that possibly the good care and food he had enjoyed throughout the winter accounted for his fine spirits. We should have knocked on wood.

One day Robert's behavior was different. He did not get up until nearly noon, and when he did come out to the kitchen, he was not interested in orange juice or toast; not even in fresh lettuce. Robert did not feel well. As the day went on, we became more concerned. Something was certainly wrong. He wanted to be held all the time. He communicated this need by backing up to a human foot, sitting down, and pushing with his tail until he was picked up and cuddled.

He wanted nothing to eat when lunch was served. Instead, he spent the time at the table nestled within the crook of Tommy's elbow, making sad little coos, not of contentment but of distress. By now there was a general feeling of anxiety throughout the household, as there is when a child is not well.

Mildred devoted herself to trying to comfort the poor little creature. When Tommy came into the house after working an hour or two in the rose garden, she said: "He wants to be held. You take him for a while."

Remembering that a letter had to be written, Tommy went to his desk, still holding Robert. He carefully put him down between his feet, forming an angle with heels together. Robert settled down, halfway resting on his side, and Tommy went on with the letter.

All of a sudden there was a high, piercing sound—a shriek. It can't be described any other way—it was a shriek.

Mildred came running in from the kitchen, and Tommy looked down in alarm, fearing that he had moved his feet and hurt the tiny creature. Then Robert stood up, shook himself, gave a contented chirp, and walked off . . . leaving an egg!

Such excitement! I was telephoned immediately, as were several other devoted friends. To our surprise, the next edition of the local paper contained an article with a large headline: ROBERT SHRIEKS, LAYS FIRST EGG. There was by this time considerable local and even statewide interest in Robert, so this was quite an achievement.

Immediately after accomplishing this feat, Robert rushed to his (excuse me, I mean HER) tray and began eating as though she had never seen food before. And how she drank! As for the egg, she could not have cared less. She completely ignored it and seemed glad that the whole business was over.

It was a full-sized egg—the real thing! When we knew that Robert did not want to have anything to do with it, the egg was carefully placed in a little velvet-lined box to be admired by many callers.

After the excitement of seeing the egg on the floor at his feet, Tommy had worn a strange half-smile on his face. Now, as he stood looking down at the velvet-lined box on the coffee table, he said, "I'm not saying 'I told you so,' but I suspected all along that Robert was a female, and now I've been proved right. Well done, Robert, well done."

Mildred had picked Robert up and murmured reassuringly, "Well, once again you have taught us something. It may take a while for us to call you 'she' instead of 'he,' but we will, we will."

Then—the discussion as to her name. Must it now be Roberta? The question answered itself. After a few half-hearted attempts to use the new name, they gave up. Robert she had always been, and Robert she would continue to be.

## Where the Sidewalk Ends

There is a place where the sidewalk ends
And before the street begins,
And there the grass grows soft and white,
And there the sun burns crimson bright,
And there the moon-bird rests from his flight
To cool in the peppermint wind.

Let us leave this place where the smoke blows black
And the dark street winds and bends.
Past the pits where the asphalt flowers grow
We shall walk with a walk that is measured and slow,
And watch where the chalk-white arrows go
To the place where the sidewalk ends.

Yes we'll walk with a walk that is measured and slow,
And we'll go where the chalk-white arrows go,
For the children, they mark, and the children, they know
The place where the sidewalk ends.

Shel Silverstein

# LITTLE RED

by Burdetta Johnson

After a jaguar had killed most of the javelina herd, Little Red was left an orphan in beautiful Hidden Canyon.

Luckily Julie Whitehead and her brother George found the little wild pigling and took him back to their Arizona ranch. There, under Julie's care and protection, he grew into a happy and healthy family pet.

As Little Red grew larger and stronger, however, he became a problem. Julie knew, before her father even made the suggestion, that it was time to take Little Red back to Hidden Canyon and a normal wilderness life.

Both Julie and George feared that Little Red would not be able to find another javelina herd or that he would be killed by the fierce jaguar that was still in the area. Even so, the time had come to return to Hidden Canyon.

On Friday afternoon when George and Julie got off the
school bus, Little Red trotted out from the gate and began
playfully circling about them.

He's only two thirds grown, Julie thought, and already
he's changed into an unpredictable animal.

Before they reached the house, George asked, "Are
you thinking about the same place I am?" He was staring
at the Santa Ritas.

Julie answered, "Hidden Canyon?"

"Yes."

"That's where he was made an orphan in the first place," she said quietly. "If that jaguar could wipe out a whole herd of javelinas, it could sure kill Little Red."

George wiped the school bus dust off his neck. "That's a chance we'll have to take. If we can get him to stay in Hidden Canyon, nobody is likely to shoot him when they're out deer hunting. If we leave him anywhere else, he'll probably follow us back to the ranch."

Julie did not want to admit it, but that made sense. They would have to push Little Red into the crack that his herd had once used as an entrance into the canyon. Then they could stack up enough rock to make a barrier so he could not get out. After he had been in the canyon a few weeks, they could remove the rocks. Chances are he would be used to wilderness life by then.

Certainly most wild pets reach a point in their growth when their instincts become stronger than their need for human companionship. They should then find their own kind and lead a normal life. But would Little Red find any javelinas now?

Both Julie and George had questioned their schoolmates, but none of them had seen any sign of a javelina lately. The drought had killed all the javelinas for miles around or had driven them from their normal habitat.

The next morning Julie was glad that neither of her parents tried to make conversation in an attempt to lift her spirits. Her mother made two lunches of peanut butter and jelly sandwiches with apples for dessert. George filled his saddle canteen with cold well water.

Shortly Julie swung atop Cowboy, and the little caravan—Cowboy, Little Red, and Chestnut—headed toward the Santa Ritas, a good two hours' riding away.

Two hours of the steady pace exhausted Little Red's enthusiasm for travel. He grunted at Julie until George dismounted and lifted him up to her.

"Have you noticed any javelina tracks?" she asked.

"Not a one," George said. "There hasn't been a javelina along here in weeks. There's not enough water in these bushes to keep a kangaroo rat alive."

That was not really true, Julie knew, since the kangaroo rats took moisture from the driest seeds. Their stomachs must be incredible, she had often reflected, but such an ability was necessary for these tiny creatures to live on the driest desert.

She was aware of moisture in her own eyes as she thought about Little Red suddenly cut off from human companionship. She would be a little reassured if she thought that Little Red could soon join a javelina herd. But—there were no javelinas left.

There weren't even many plants left down here on the flats. Some of them—the poppies and the tender flowers— had long since dried up. Other plants had dropped their leaves and taken a long rest during the dry weather. The cactus fought the drought with spongy stems and roots that held the water in a sheath of waxy skin. The desert trees fought the effects of the drought with widespread root systems that reached deep into the earth and soaked up all the moisture that could be found.

The javelinas had no such means of getting water from the dry land. If they couldn't find a habitat with moisture, they would die.

"What about jaguar tracks?" Julie asked.

"There wouldn't be any out here where it's so dry," George answered. "Wait'll we get up in the scrub oak."

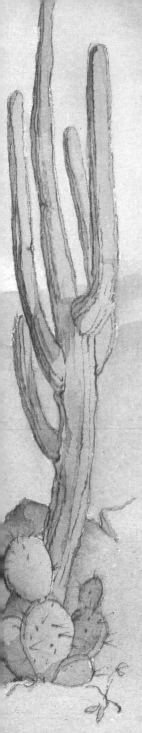

But there were none there either. Julie really did not expect any, although she scanned the ground on both sides of her pony. There were not even many animal wastes. Once she spotted some displaced leaves, and she reined Cowboy toward them to see if there might be a lion or jaguar scraping. It turned out to be the scratching left by wild turkeys hunting acorns. She identified their tracks in a dust spot—three toes forward and one back, as if a pencil had been pressed into the dirt to make them.

Little Red had enough of the swinging ride. He grunted to indicate that he wanted to walk again. Julie leaned down and let him slide to the ground.

A few minutes later the little caravan arrived at the dark crack that was the entrance into Hidden Canyon. Neither Julie nor her brother had ever had any desire to explore this black place. The pathway they usually took, higher up the mountain slope, allowed enough light for safe climbing, and there was little chance of stumbling over a snake.

There was no water in the rocky streambed below them. In normal weather, the water from Hidden Canyon bubbled up through the sand and ran along the streambed for several hundred yards before seeping back into the ground.

"Do you suppose there's water in there?" Julie asked with uncertainty as they stood before the crack.

"I can hear a waterfall. It's probably not very big, but it's there."

Moving quickly before she had a chance to burst out crying, Julie shoved the surprised Little Red into the darkness and held him there while George stacked loose rock in the entrance. Within a few minutes he had made a barrier as high as their heads, completely filling the

two-foot-wide crack. The bewildered Little Red stood in
the darkness behind the stones, grunting displeasure at
the harsh treatment.

In an apparent effort to get Julie away from this
situation, which seemed about ready to bring a flood of
tears, George said, "Let's climb up and look in the
canyon. We can call Little Red from up there and coax
him to come on through."

They led Cowboy and Chestnut at a fast walk up the
slope. Julie sensed that her brother was as glad as she
was to get beyond the range of Little Red's pleading
squeals.

"What if the jaguar happens to show up like it did
before?" she asked as they neared the cleft.

"There's about as much chance of that as there is of lightning striking the same place twice."

They were only a few yards from the place where they could leave the horses, when Chestnut jerked her head high and pranced away from a pile of leaves.

"What's the matter with her?" Julie asked.

"I don't know." George handed Chestnut's reins to Julie before stepping forward to see what had frightened the horse.

He raked the leaves aside with a stick. "It's part of a javelina," he said quietly. "It's been dead less than a couple of days."

Julie watched him bend close to the ground.

"What's the matter?"

He paused before answering. "What's the biggest mountain lion track you ever heard of?"

"Four inches maybe."

George straightened and looked at her. "There's a cat track here that's a lot bigger than that."

Dropping the reins of both mounts, Julie scrambled to George's side. "It's a jaguar track, isn't it?" she asked.

"It sure looks like it."

"Do you suppose a jaguar's been using the canyon, too?"

George glanced toward the cleft that was their route into the canyon. "Well, there's no place else around here where there's any water to amount to anything. If there are any javelinas still left in this part of the country, chances are they're in the canyon."

"What are we going to do?" Julie knew her voice sounded hopeless, but she didn't care.

George studied the jaguar's kill while he considered this. "Well, it's broad daylight," he said. "A jaguar is not going to stir around before dark unless it's forced to. Chances are it's holed up in some old mine tunnel around here, or maybe back in the rocks somewhere. We can find out if it's been in the canyon lately."

Julie needed no more urging. "Come on," she said. "Let's let Cowboy and Chestnut drag reins. They can't go far."

Julie led the scramble up the steep pathway through the cleft. She was not as careful as she should have been to look where she put her hands, but fortunately there were no rattlers near the rocky ledges she used as hand-holds. It took only a few minutes to make the climb.

They were both breathless by the time they got to the top, but they didn't wait to catch a breath. Julie plodded doggedly across the cliff top to the canyon's rim. There she dropped to all fours, and George settled beside her. Both scanned the narrow canyon floor below.

The summer drought had had only a slight effect on this natural garden. Last winter's snow had soaked enough moisture into the slopes above to provide steady seeping. Underground rock channeled enough of this moisture into Hidden Canyon to provide a water supply.

The array of plant growth below was still green. A few of the tropical trees were beginning to drop their shiny red leaves. But along the stream the trees were as green and full as they had ever been.

"Let's climb down and look," Julie suggested. The canyon appeared peaceful enough, but it was impossible to detect any sign of a jaguar from this distance.

As she climbed down to the first ledge, a flutter in one of the bushes below caught her eye. It was a rose-throated becard, a big-headed tropical bird with a thick bill, which looked much like a flycatcher. The bird had been considered extinct in the United States until a few years ago, but Julie had seen two of their nests here in the canyon.

Halfway down, an Arizona woodpecker flared up from scrub oaks across the canyon. But Julie had no thoughts for these unusual birds now. Her attention was poised for the slightest movement of wildlife on the canyon floor. As soon as she stepped off the last ledge, she bent to examine the sandy floor. It was covered with fallen leaves and dead twigs and revealed no tracks.

Turning her face toward the canyon's lower end, she cupped her hands around her mouth and shouted, "Little Red!"

The shout generated a squeal and rustling of leaves a few yards up canyon. Whirling in surprise, Julie glimpsed George jerking his knife from its sheath.

There was no danger, however. Rapidly disappearing lean hips identified several javelinas bobbing up canyon. One apparently was a female, since Julie saw two piglings racing in her tracks. The piglings were only a few weeks old, not an unusual situation here where javelinas were born in any month. Two more javelinas seemed to be nearly grown. They were probably as old as Little Red.

George returned the knife to its sheath and followed Julie's example of shouting to encourage Little Red on through the natural tunnel and into the canyon.

"Let's climb back up on a ledge where we can see him when he comes out," George suggested. The two found an observation point about fifteen feet above the canyon floor, which allowed them to see where Little Red would emerge into the canyon. It took only a few more calls to get the desired response.

"There he comes," Julie said as Little Red's figure burst from the dark crack. "He sure is running hard."

"Listen to him squeal."

"Maybe he's happy about not getting left behind."

"He doesn't sound happy. He sounds scared."

"Little Red's not scared of anything." Julie had just got the words from her mouth when she saw something that made her grab George's arm. But George had seen it, too.

"The jaguar," he gasped. "Let's get out of here!"

Julie reacted with more loyalty to Little Red than with common sense. "We can't leave him here to get killed. That jaguar must have been waiting in there when Little Red ran past it."

George seized her wrist. "Are you crazy! That's a jaguar, not a mountain lion. It would just as soon turn on us as on a javelina. Get to climbing!"

There was nothing they could do, Julie realized. Maybe Little Red could find a hole the jaguar couldn't get into. But her gaze seemed fixed on the chase. She stared without moving as the jaguar followed Little Red in a running crouch, its stomach close to the ground. The wildly fleeing Little Red stayed only a few steps in front.

"Move, Julie!" George screamed, shoving her forward toward the route upward. Julie, reacting against her brother's firm command, slapped his arm down.

Her action was unfortunate, however. She stumbled, and before she could recover her balance, she rolled off the ledge and slid down the steep slope. She came to a stop in the leaves of the canyon floor, which was no more than ten steps wide at this point.

"Get up that tree!" George yelled.

But there was no time. As she pulled herself up to hands and knees, Little Red darted past her, kicking up leaves and sand with each footstep.

The jaguar stopped abruptly in the little clearing. Uncertainty lasted only a moment. Then it stalked toward Julie, its upper lip drawn back over its teeth, a sight that held her paralyzed with fear.

She later remembered seeing George scrambling down toward her, his hunting knife in hand.

The next minute was the longest one Julie had ever known. She recalled later the quick chain of events, like scenes in a movie rushing past at high speed. Everything seemed to be happening at once, so fast that it was impossible to remember what happened first.

The jaguar had slowed to a walking crouch, its tail curled to either side like that of a house cat stalking a mouse or a bird. Its ears no longer leaned forward in alertness but were laid back against its head as if they had been trimmed away.

Its teeth were like ivory daggers, and later Julie remembered the terror that was generated by the sight of

those same teeth against the animal's black lips. The daggerlike teeth seemed as long and as thick as her own fingers.

Somehow she was aware of each claw reaching from its sheath atop a toe. This was the animal that could break a deer's back with a single blow.

For the first time in her life Julie saw the effect of camouflage. The jaguar—one of the most feared cats in all the world—could hide behind its spotted coat. The spots destroyed the animal's outline. She could see spots, but they were moving spots, and the jaguar's legs and head were lost in the changing pattern.

George was at her side now. His hunting knife was pointed forward in his right hand, and his left was scraping up a handful of sand.

What really seemed unreal, however, was Little Red. That fleeing creature had turned in time to sense Julie's danger and had trotted back with angry grunts and clicking teeth.

He came to a stop at Julie's side, his hair sticking straight up as if he were a furious porcupine. His mouth was open, and Julie saw his own tusks poised for action. They were half as long as the jaguar's teeth.

This unexpected array seemed to puzzle the jaguar for a moment. The prey was too scattered to be killed in a single sweep. George, with his shining hunting knife and threatening crouch, apparently presented the greatest danger.

The jaguar turned toward him. Julie saw its rear legs lift slowly as the muscles gathered. Its body twisted slightly and settled back onto rear legs. Julie knew she should dodge away, but her body would not act.

George acted. He flung the handful of sand in an underhand motion, as he had done so often as a softball pitcher.

The jaguar had not expected such a move. The sand caught it full in the eyes.

This was all that Little Red needed. With the jaguar shaking its head furiously to clear its vision, Little Red charged the unprotected side and swept on beneath the

cat. When he emerged on the other side Julie saw that the handsome spotted coat had been neatly parted by Little Red's tusks.

The jaguar had no forewarning of this attack. With sand still clouding its vision, the cat whirled and began striking out blindly in all directions.

Little Red stayed beyond the range of the sharp claws, and his squeals drove the maddened jaguar to even greater effort.

The shifting Little Red could not be touched.

Little Red did not close with the jaguar again until it collapsed, its strength having given way. Then Little Red charged the fallen cat, shredding the spotted coat along its sides.

George was sitting alongside Julie, a weak grin on his pale face, when the fury inside Little Red began to weaken. The young javelina, exhausted but eyes sparkling, stopped to gasp for breath. Julie realized then that she was weak, too, and she slid forward onto her stomach.

"George," she said after a while. "Did Little Red really do that?"

George looked at the knife still in his hand. "He sure did."

Now Julie's eyes were on the javelina. "Little Red," she said softly. "Come here and let me see if you are all right."

But the excitement of battle had not completely left the javelina. Julie sensed that the past moment had brought Little Red very close to the wilderness life of his kind. When he had whirled about to protect his human companions, he had not acted through loyalty. He had acted instinctively.

Now, however, Julie saw that a new instinct had gripped Little Red. His head lifted, and she could see that he was feeling the air for a new scent.

Ignoring Julie and her brother, Little Red trotted past and pushed his nose into a javelina track. Then he examined another, and still another, as his breath puffed dust from them.

Julie heard Little Red grunting softly. It revealed an excitement she had never detected in him before. It was a sound of triumph.

She tried once more. "Little Red," Julie pleaded. "Come over here to me."

But Little Red had no thoughts for her. His nose lifted from the tracks, and he looked up canyon. Without waiting he started off, his movement awkward but triumphant.

"You know what?" Julie asked after a while.

"What?"

"I don't think we'll need to keep those rocks piled up down there in that tunnel."

George grinned. "I think we ought to take them down on our way home."

Julie had one more question. "How long do you think it will be before Little Red becomes the herd leader of the javelinas?"

George looked up canyon, but there was no sign of a disappearing animal. "Well, judging by the way Little Red piles into anything he starts, I think it won't be too long."

# Moosik

by Vera Chaplina

Moosik, a rhesus monkey, was so tiny when he was born that Ekaterina Andreyevna, the head keeper of the Monkey House, didn't even notice him at first. He held on tightly to his mother and pressed so close to her that he was almost overlooked.

He was Miki's first baby, and perhaps that was why she was so nervous. Instead of feeding her offspring, she just kept looking around in a very troubled way and covered the baby with her arms.

When Ekaterina Andreyevna came in and offered Miki an apple, the monkey uttered a frightened cry and crawled up to the very top of the cage. This behavior troubled the keeper, who had worked with monkeys for over twenty years and knew their habits thoroughly. She felt certain that Miki would not be a good mother. And she was right.

Day by day Miki ate less and less. She sat on the top beam, coming down only after all the other monkeys had gone. Then, clutching Moosik tightly to her, she would climb down cautiously, snatch up a piece of bread or a bit of porridge and quickly return to her place on the ledge. She only got the scraps, since the choice bits had already been eaten by the other monkeys.

The attendants tried several times to put Miki in a separate cage where she could be alone, but they didn't succeed. Catching a monkey with a little baby in a huge cage wasn't an easy matter. There was always the danger that she might drop and injure the little one. So Miki was left in the common cage but was very closely watched.

Miki continued to lose weight, and to make matters worse, she developed a bad cold. She could not produce enough milk for her baby, and each day Moosik got thinner and thinner. Finally he was so hungry that even though he was supposed to have only milk, he would stick his tiny hands into Miki's mouth while she was eating to try to get some food.

The superintendent consulted with Ekaterina and the vet and decided that in spite of the risk, they would have to take the baby away from Miki.

All the necessary preparations were made by Ekaterina. She spread a thick layer of straw over the floor of the cage so that if Moosik should fall, he would not injure himself. When the ladders and perches were removed, the chase began.

An attempt to catch Miki with a hoop net failed completely. She tore through the members of the group like an arrow, clambered up on the screening and, giving herself a push, bounced like a ball to the other side of the cage. The prospects of catching her looked very dim. But during one of Miki's wild leaps, she loosened her hold on the baby and dropped him. Everyone was certain that he had been killed, but fortunately, he fell on the straw that had been piled on the floor.

Before Ekaterina could get to him, one of the monkeys snatched him up and ran off with him. The attendants managed to catch them both in the hoop net just as they were climbing up the screening.

Feeling around gently in the net for the baby, they lifted him out and gave him to Ekaterina, who carefully tucked him into the folds of her warm, knitted jacket. A few moments before, Moosik had held on tightly to the unfamiliar monkey as if she were his mother. Now, when he felt the warmth of Ekaterina's jacket, he clung just as tightly to her and calmed down.

The vet who was standing by while all this took place wanted to examine Moosik to see if he had been hurt, but Moosik was comfortable where he was and had no desire to leave Ekaterina. He had not been injured in the fall—not even bruised.

This tiny, two-week-old monkey was a pitiful sight, with his head only slightly larger than a walnut, his wrinkled face, and arms that looked like twigs. He pressed close to Ekaterina, and whenever anyone tried to look at him, he hid his head and squealed.

"He knew the right one to come to," laughed the vet. "Shall we put him with the nurslings, or shall we take him to the medical section?"

"How about my taking him home with me?" asked Ekaterina. In the few minutes that the monkey had clung to her, she had begun to feel a surge of pity for the little fellow and wanted very much to take care of him.

"That's not a bad idea," responded the superintendent, and turning to the vet, he added, "There'll be many problems with this little fellow. He'll have to be kept warm and watched through the night. Ekaterina Andreyevna has had many years of experience with monkeys. She'll know what to do."

The vet agreed, and Moosik remained with Ekaterina.

## Troubles

Ekaterina Andreyevna knew that she was in for trouble when she took this two-week-old monkey. To begin with, he refused to eat. As soon as they got home she warmed up some milk for him. She poured it into a bottle, put a nipple on the bottle, and offered it to him. Moosik turned his head away, refusing even to look at it. Next, she tried feeding him from a teaspoon, but he wouldn't take it that way either. When she forcibly poured a little milk into his mouth, he spit it out. She tried to sweeten the milk, then to dilute it. She even added heavy cream, but Moosik would have none of it.

Worn out after a night of struggling, Ekaterina could scarcely wait for morning to come, when she could consult with the vet and the superintendent.

When they did arrive, the first thing the superintendent asked was, "How did it go?"

"Very badly. I tried everything I could think of, but he wouldn't take a drop of milk." With a helpless motion of her hands she pointed to the disorderly room. The table was completely covered with cups, saucers, bottles, milk mixtures, large and small nipples, spoons, and medicine droppers. Everything was in disarray. And the cause of all this confusion was nestling in the folds of Ekaterina's warm jacket, thoroughly content.

"I see you had a hard night," said the vet, shaking her head as she surveyed the room. She knew that Ekaterina had done all that anyone could be expected to do. "Well, let's try again."

All three of them began coaxing the little fellow to eat, but no matter how or what they tried, they did not succeed. They knew that he would have to be made to eat to keep up his strength, so they began to offer him all sorts of things. And of all the many foods he was given, surprisingly enough he accepted orange juice. But that was all that he would take. After several days, Ekaterina trained Moosik to drink milk. From then on, the little fellow began to get stronger.

As he grew bigger he was given bits of apple and crusts of white bread soaked in milk, as well as other foods necessary for a monkey's growth. Moosik didn't eat everything with equal relish. He liked all sorts of juices, ate porridge with some enjoyment, but refused to swallow cod-liver oil. Ekaterina had a hard time making him take even a few drops. She tried diluting the cod-liver oil in orange juice, but that brought no success.

The prospects for training Moosik were not encouraging, either. For instance, Moosik hated to be left alone, and his favorite spot was still in the folds of Ekaterina's jacket. Moosik had a small cage of his own that looked something like a child's bed. It had a soft feather puff under which a hot-water bottle had been placed to keep him warm. But whenever Ekaterina tried to put him down in it, Moosik shrieked loudly and clung to anything he could get hold of with his tiny hands. Ekaterina would have to take him in her arms again.

## The Prankster

Moosik was full of mischief. While he was a baby Ekaterina put up with his pranks, but as he grew older the pranks became harder to overlook.

When Ekaterina took up her knitting, Moosik would snatch her glasses off her nose or pull out one of her needles and ruin her work.

When Ekaterina sat down to dinner, Moosik would grab the spoon from her mouth and pour the soup all over her dress.

One day Ekaterina thought that Moosik ought to have some toys. Since he didn't like being left alone, she took him along with her when she went to the store. Moosik settled himself so deep into the folds of her coat collar that no one could see him, not even the man sitting next to them in the bus.

At the store Ekaterina asked to be shown some toys. She looked them over but couldn't seem to find what she considered suitable for Moosik. The clerk had laid before her a pile of toy ducks, dogs, fish, teddy bears, and even rattles. Ekaterina couldn't make up her mind.

Finally, somewhat impatiently, the clerk said, "I don't know what else to show you. These are our most popular toys for a little child."

"Oh, yes, but you see, this child isn't like that. He's . . ."

"Oh, a spoiled child," said the clerk, finishing the sentence for Ekaterina. "I understand. Perhaps you'd like a windup toy."

"No, you see . . ." Ekaterina began again, not knowing how to tell the clerk that the toy was for a monkey. But she didn't have to tell her—Moosik solved that problem. Tired of being in the dark, he cautiously pushed his little face out from the coat, saw the pile of shining toys, and hopped out onto the counter in a twinkling.

No need to say that the clerk was surprised and confused. Moosik, however, wasn't in the least confused. He dug among the toys, grabbed a big red ring with a bright green rattle, and scrambled back to Ekaterina's coat.

The clerk regained her poise only after Moosik had
disappeared with his prize. She laughed heartily with the
customers over the way Moosik had selected his own toy.

One could never tell how Moosik would behave when
he was taken into a store. Once he snatched at the glasses
of a woman standing nearby. The woman did not get
angry, and in fact, she even offered Moosik some candy,
but his pranks did cause Ekaterina a great deal of
embarrassment.

Things were becoming more and more difficult at home, too. Now that he was bigger, he was no longer content to sit in the folds of Ekaterina's jacket. He clambered around, keeping fairly close to her. If he happened to come upon something he was forbidden to touch, Ekaterina would get up and go to the door as if she were going out. Moosik would abandon the object and tear after her, clinging to her dress and shrieking wildly. In time the little prankster caught on to this trick, and he no longer ran after Ekaterina when she pretended to be going out. Instead, he just watched very carefully until she was about to disappear behind the door. Then he would take off after her, clinging so tightly to her dress that it was almost impossible to get him loose.

As each day passed, Moosik was becoming more skillful at climbing and leaping. He was able to climb up on the curtains and jump easily from there onto the bookshelves or the bed. Everything that was not needed had been removed from the room. Ekaterina Andreyevna had long since taken away the tiny statue from the table, as well as the mirror, bottles, combs, and handbags—everything that could attract the monkey's curiosity. Moosik had already broken a number of Ekaterina's belongings. Finally the day came when he climbed up into the cupboard and threw all the dishes onto the floor. Ekaterina realized that it was time to part with him.

## In New Surroundings

At first the plan was to put Moosik back in the Monkey House, but then it was decided to place him in the Exhibition Center. There were all sorts of animals in this section—wolves, foxes, porcupines, peacocks, and many others. They were all tame, and every one of them could be picked up and handled freely.

Visitors never came to this part of the zoo. These were the animals that were occasionally taken to schools, clubs, or parks to be exhibited while a lecturer spoke on the life and habits of the animals.

The head of the Exhibition Center was Galina, and it was to her that Moosik was entrusted.

So that Moosik could get accustomed to Galina and not suffer too much from his separation from Ekaterina, he was not transferred at once. Galina began visiting him, bringing along ripe bananas or a bunch of grapes. She took time to play with him. And yet, in spite of all the preparation, the transfer to the new place proved to be a very unhappy experience for Moosik. He refused to eat. He cried and tried to get out of his cage. Only when there were attendants around did he feel at ease.

## In Training

When Moosik finally got accustomed to his new home, Galina put him in the charge of a young biology student, Olya, whose responsibility it was to keep a detailed record of his development.

After a time Olya decided to teach Moosik to sit in a chair and eat with a spoon. Some of the students made him a chair and table that were just the right size. When they presented him with the furniture, Moosik showed great interest in it. He climbed on the table, sat there for a while, got down, turned it upside down, and began to chew on one of the legs. To prevent this, the students smeared mustard over the legs. After one taste, Moosik made a face and never touched it again.

Olya sat Moosik down on the chair next to the table and said, "Sit, Moosik." Then she gave him a lump of sugar. But the monkey had no intention of sitting. As soon as he ate the sugar, he jumped off the chair and clambered up on Olya, looking for more.

He got no sugar from Olya. She sat him down again, saying, "Sit, Moosik, sit there," and only after he sat down did she give him another lump. He caught on quickly as to what was expected of him. By the third lesson when he was told to sit, he obeyed and waited expectantly for his reward.

Teaching him to eat from a spoon was much more difficult. He held the spoon readily enough, but whenever the bowl was set before him, he threw the spoon away and put both hands into the bowl.

Olya didn't know what to do to prevent this. She had become annoyed and would shove the spoon back into his hand, whereupon Moosik would become angry, shriek loudly, and throw the spoon away again.

"You mustn't get so impatient, Olya," said Galina. She had come in to see how things were going and noticed at once that Olya was having problems. "You must be calm and even-tempered in dealing with animals, otherwise your lessons will be worthless. You'll have to think of some way to make Moosik hold a spoon."

Galina then reminded her of Moosik's attraction for bright objects and suggested that she replace the metal spoon with a colored plastic one.

The very next day Olya bought a bright blue spoon and brought it to the zoo. As soon as she showed it to Moosik, he grabbed it and wouldn't let go. When Olya set a bowl of grape juice in front of him, he held on firmly to the spoon. Carefully guiding it to the bowl, Olya helped the monkey to use the spoon properly.

It took only a few days for him to be able to feed himself easily. He liked the spoon so much that he tried to carry it off with him. Whenever he could, he would sleep with it.

Teaching Moosik to "read" a book was easy. Of course, this really meant just turning the pages, but it gave the impression that he was reading. The book was fairly large and had wooden pages. Olya put it on the table before him and placed a cookie between the pages, letting Moosik see what she was doing. The monkey immediately turned the page, found the cookie, and ate it. It took him no time at all to master this trick. One day when he had been permitted to go alone into one of the rooms, he "read" all the books and magazines on the tables, leaving them torn to bits.

After demonstrating his ability to perform several tricks, Moosik was ready for exhibition. At first he was shown in his cage, but later, when he had become accustomed to the program, Galina would take him out and hold him in her arms as she lectured.

## A Reunion

A year had gone by. During all this time Ekaterina had not visited her pet even once. She had received reports from Galina about Moosik and knew that he had grown and that he wasn't lonely. She didn't want to upset him but wanted very much to see Moosik without his seeing her.

One day there was to be an exhibition of tame animals in the zoo auditorium. When Ekaterina heard about it,

she decided to take a chance and have a look at her nursling. As it happened, she came in late and just at the very moment that Moosik, seated at his table, was demonstrating his ability to use a spoon, she was getting into her seat. The sound attracted the monkey's attention. He turned his head and recognized her. Propelling his whole body forward, he forcibly pushed the dish aside and, with the blue spoon still in hand, ran right through the rows of people, straight to Ekaterina. He clung to her neck, holding on so tightly that it was impossible to pull him away.

Together they went up on the stage of the auditorium, and instead of giving the lecture that she had prepared, Galina substituted the story of Moosik. It wasn't necessary for her to say that he had remembered Ekaterina. The audience had witnessed that meeting themselves.

BELMONT PARK OCT.30.1910.

# Heroines of the Sky

by Jean Adams and Margaret Kimball

With eyes fixed on the pilot, Harriet Quimby followed the steady ascent of the plane. As she watched, the wind-blown figure sitting there between the struts became a mere blob, then a nothing, finally disappearing behind outspread wings. She thought of the airplane as an eagle, soaring to its mountaintop, loosening all ties with the earth. Perhaps it was at this moment that Harriet Quimby first knew what she most wanted in life.

The sky above Belmont Park was sunny on that October afternoon in 1910, but a few clouds raced before the stiff breeze, whipping at the flags of many nations—among them the Stars and Stripes. How could anyone possibly fly to the Statue of Liberty in such a wind?

That October afternoon marked the end of America's first international air meet. Along with a crowd of about fifty thousand people, Harriet had watched air pilots from different parts of the world take off from Belmont Park on a flight to the Statue of Liberty—some seventeen miles away—and back again. Now she watched breathlessly as the last pilot, an American, climbed into the open plane. Then came the whir of the propeller, and John Moisant began his ascent. Could he establish the speed record for America? Harriet dared hope. Then at the first sight of his returning plane, she cheered wildly. John Moisant had won the race! The young pilot had set a new record, flying the thirty-four miles in about the same number of minutes.

Then and there Harriet Quimby made up her mind that she would learn to fly. She returned to her job at *Leslie's Weekly*, and it was not until the following summer that the young magazine writer set about to accomplish her dream.

In the meanwhile, John Moisant had crashed to his death, and though she had never met him in person, she shared the sorrow of others who had thrilled to his exploits. Before his death, John Moisant had established a flying school at Garden City, Long Island, and it was here that Harriet applied for instruction.

"I suppose it seems a little odd—for me—a woman," she said to the young man who received her.

"Not at all." He smiled back. "The fact is that Miss Matilde Moisant has already started lessons."

Harriet's thoughts flashed back to the international races, where she had seen two slight, dark-haired girls rushing forward to greet John Moisant after he returned from his successful flight. Someone had said the girls were his sisters. Perhaps Harriet may have felt a little envious. Matilde Moisant had already started flying lessons. This meant that she herself would not be the first qualified woman pilot in the United States.

Might *Leslie's Weekly* object to her new undertaking? Might they fear that flying lessons would distract her from her work? Fearful of this, the girl arranged to have her lessons at dawn. Her instructor, André Houpert, was also teaching Matilde Moisant, and very soon he arranged a meeting between his two pupils.

Although the two young women would have liked each other anyway, their friendship was quickly established by their one common enthusiasm. Propellers and engines, struts and wires—such words were shuttled between them as freely as were pop tunes and football scores among their friends. Yet underneath, they were friendly rivals who had fixed their hearts on the same goal. Which would be the first to qualify for a pilot's license?

For some unexplained reason it was Harriet who succeeded first. On August 2, 1911, America could boast a licensed woman pilot for the first time. The honor had come to Harriet Quimby after thirty-three lessons—a flying time of four and one-half hours.

Two weeks later, on August 17, Matilde received her pilot's license. To Matilde, this date was not as important as her trial date had been—August 13. For was not thirteen her lucky number? Born September 13, 1886, she decided to name her plane *Lucky Thirteen*.

On her twenty-fifth birthday, September 13, 1911, Matilde took *Lucky Thirteen* on a cross-country flight. In

*Matilde Moisant*

those days every flier made this gesture. It was like saying to the world, "See, I'm a real aviator." In Matilde's case the gesture was convincing, for during this flight she set the women's altitude record. It was 1,500 feet! People today may not be impressed by this height, but in 1911 it caused a great deal of excitement; and Matilde Moisant's name became known all over the country. Later, she became the first woman to fly over Mexico City. The date? Why, of course, it was on November 13 of the same year. For this feat she received $490.

Meanwhile, the ambitious Harriet Quimby was not marking time. Just two days after receiving her pilot's license, she made a moonlight flight above Staten Island. Twenty thousand people were present to exclaim over the daring exploit. For was not this the first time an American woman had turned nightingale?

Still greater crowds turned out to watch her exhibition flights at the Richmond County Fair. It was then that she first donned the spectacular flying costume in which she later made all her important flights. The trousers tucked into high laced boots, and the blouse with long sleeves, choker collar, and hood were made of mauve-colored satin. By no means was this costume typical of the day. Did not her friend Matilde Moisant fly in a divided skirt? Undoubtedly there were envious people in the crowd who asked, "Does she think she's going up in the air or on the stage?"

By the autumn of that year both Matilde and Harriet were making exhibition flights over Mexico and parts of America. Thousands of people always gathered to watch them—the ambitious young flier in her mauve-colored satin and the dark-haired pilot in her divided skirt. Sometimes, too, the audience got an unexpected thrill. Once Harriet's plane balked when she was only a hundred and fifty feet above the ground, and it was skillful maneuvering alone that enabled her to make a successful landing.

The very next day Matilde had a more serious mishap. Her plane crashed, and with difficulty she escaped from its wreckage.

"Good old *Lucky Thirteen*," she may have murmured as she pulled herself out.

At the same time Harriet may have said, "Better not depend too much on your old thirteen. You're awfully careless—you know you are, Matilde."

Although Harriet was much more careful than her friend about going over her machine before starting, she was not above superstition. She always wore with her mauve-colored satin an antique necklace and bracelet that were supposed to bring good luck.

By this time *Leslie's Weekly* was fully aware of the spectacular role their young writer was playing in the air.

Far from discouraging her, they played up her activities, and when she undertook the most ambitious exploit of her career, they made only one request: She should give them first rights to a story of her adventure.

And what was the adventure to which Harriet had now set herself? It was the crossing of the English Channel—a feat not yet accomplished by any woman pilot. She was going to fly for the first time in her life a Blériot monoplane. She was going to fly—also for the first time—across water. She was going to dare what no woman had ever dared before.

Never before this time had she used a compass. But now, since everyone insisted that it would be madness to attempt the Channel without this instrument, she received some instructions in its use from an aviator named Hamel. It was Hamel, in fact, who sent her off with the warning, "Whatever you do, Miss Quimby, keep to your course. If you get five miles out of the way, you will be over the North Sea, and you know what that means."

Well indeed she did know. But if any fearful thought was in her mind, she did not show it on that morning of April 16, 1912, when she stood on the white cliffs of Dover and smiled at the group that had gathered about her. Over there lay the coast of France—she would think of nothing else.

She and her mechanic went over every part of the plane. Then she got into her open seat—the cockpit was not to come for several more years—and waved her hand. There was a last flashing smile, and then she was off—without parachute or any of the instruments used today. The following is taken from Harriet's own description of her trip, very much as it appeared in *Leslie's Weekly:*

I was hardly out of sight of the cheering crowd before I hit a fog bank and found my needle of invaluable assistance. I could not see above, below, or ahead. I ascended to a height of 6,000 feet, hoping to escape the mist that surrounded me. It was bitter cold—the kind of cold that chills to the bone. I recalled somewhat nervously Hamel's remark about the North Sea, but a glance at my compass reassured me that I was within my course. Failing to strike clear air, I determined to descend again. It was then that I came near a mishap. The machine tilted to a steep angle, causing the gasoline to flood, and my engine began to misfire. I figured on pancaking down so as to strike the water with the plane in a floating position. But, greatly to my relief, the gasoline quickly burned out, and my engine began to purr evenly. A glance at the watch on my wrist reminded me that I should be near the French coast. Soon a gleaming strip of white sand flashed by, green grass caught my eyes, and I knew I was within my goal.

Yes, she was within sight of her goal, and a few minutes later she was to touch down near a small French village. There she was welcomed by a crowd of wondering fisherfolk, who warmed her with tea and tried desperately to make her understand their French. It was not until she got back to England that she was to hear that another aviator who had attempted to cross the Channel that day had been lost. He had been pulled out of his course and over the North Sea.

A heroine! Yes, she became that both in England and in America.

Once back in New York, she slipped into her routine duties at *Leslie's Weekly*. But doubtless she had a feeling of restlessness. She had performed the most daring feat ever undertaken by a woman pilot. Now what? Shuttling between her office and the hotel where she lived with the devoted mother who was so proud of her success, Harriet must have sighed for new worlds to conquer.

In an article Harriet wrote for *Good Housekeeping Magazine*, she stated, "Only a cautious person—man or woman—should fly." She never mounted her machine until every part was tested. She had never had an accident in the air. It may have been luck, but she believed it to be the care given by a good mechanic.

A good mechanic was with her on July 1, 1912, when she entered an air meet at Boston. He had gone over every part of her machine while she watched. Even so, with a bit of superstition, she may have touched her antique necklace and bracelet. All right now. Ready. She turned her dazzling smile to the thousands of people. Then she mounted the pilot's seat. Even from a distance the mauve-colored satin of her costume stood out against the flaming gold of the sunset sky.

She carried with her a passenger—Mr. William Willard, manager of the air meet. A beautiful ascent above Boston Harbor was followed by a swift downward swoop, then—horror showed in every eye as Mr. Willard was thrown from the plane. Another second and Harriet fell to the water beneath. She was gone—gone only eleven months after she had received her license.

No one could explain the cause of the tragedy. Had something gone wrong with the engine? Had Harriet fainted when the plane made the swift downward swoop? It is possible that contact with a pocket of air had unseated her passenger. Since he replaced the bag of sand that her Blériot monoplane required for balance, his fall may have so upset this balance that she, too, was jerked from her seat.

Whatever the cause of the tragedy, America was saddened by the death of one of its great aviators. And what of Matilde Moisant? She had been in the air meet, too, flying in formation with Harriet when the tragedy took place. She had seen the two bodies whirl to the water, and it took all the willpower she had to guide her plane back to the earth.

She later told a reporter, "How I wish somebody could tell me it wasn't true—Miss Quimby's death. No accident except my brother Jack's ever affected me so much." Then she added, "When I think how she was always scolding me for my carelessness, and here I am after all my accidents, while she had to die in her first mishap."

Certainly if there was anyone who had experienced many accidents, it was Matilde Moisant. She had escaped from a wrecked plane while she and Harriet Quimby were giving exhibition flights in Mexico. This, however, was merely a forerunner of other narrow escapes. Some weeks after Harriet Quimby's death, Matilde had another major accident. While flying close to the ground, her plane struck a knoll. The machine turned completely over, and she was pinned underneath.

"I escaped with a bruised face," she reported with typical merriment. "I think it was my size that saved me. But oh, if it had been a biplane, then nothing could have saved me."

A few days later she was flying again. No thought of earlier mishaps clouded her face. A big crowd of people had watched her ascend, and when she attempted to land, they pressed forward. She had only a second to decide what she must do. To avoid flying into the crowd she would have to risk her own life. For Matilde Moisant there was no choice.

She turned on the spark and tried to ascend. But the machine shot up only thirty feet before it came down. It fell with such force that the oil tanks were loosened. Immediately the whole ship was ablaze. The crowd rushed forward. They did not expect to see Matilde Moisant alive. They stared as a tiny figure emerged from the blaze as if they were seeing a ghost. Could this be the work of her lucky thirteen?

"Will you please telephone my sister?" said Matilde Moisant quietly. "She may be worried about me."

That was her final appearance in the air. She did not retire because she had lost her courage, but because she could no longer bear the suffering she imposed upon her family. So she did as they requested. She retired to a ranch. Matilde Moisant would no longer be conquering the dangers of the sky. At the age of twenty-six her career in the air was over.

Seventeen years later an attendant at the airport in Oakland, California, approached a woman of forty-three who was gazing hungrily at the airplanes taking off and landing. Watching her face closely, he mentioned the pleasures of flying into the heavens. "Really, madam, you don't know what life is all about until you've gone up."

The woman bought a ticket and walked out to a biplane where the propeller was slowly ticking over. Glancing over the ship, she climbed into the front cockpit.

"Now don't be afraid, madam," said the pilot. "Just relax and enjoy yourself."

Matilde Moisant said nothing. But she smiled as she looked down on the town they were circling. This was not the windblown, dangerous flight that she and Harriet Quimby had experienced when they rode out in the open between the struts of the world's early airplanes. Sitting here in a cockpit was as cozy as a hotel room!

# Buddies

by Howard Liss

It was the final game of the 1958 basketball season for the Minneapolis Lakers and the Cincinnati Royals. The game meant little to the Lakers, for they had not qualified for the play-offs. But the Royals had won a spot in the post-season series, and they were playing hard, preparing for the tough games ahead.

Most of the fans were watching Maurice "Big Mo" Stokes, Cincinnati's great sharpshooter. Two years earlier, he had been Rookie of the Year, and during the 1958 season he had already scored more than 1,000 points. Stokes was having his usual hot game when suddenly he tripped and fell, hitting his head on the hardwood floor. He was knocked unconscious and lay motionless for several minutes.

"How are you feeling, Mo?" asked teammate Jack Twyman when Mo regained consciousness.

"I've felt better." Stokes grinned sheepishly and said, "I just needed a little sleep, that's all."

Three days later, in Detroit, the Cincinnati Royals lost a play-off game and were out of the series. Stokes played hard but scored only a dozen points. Following the Detroit game, he complained of headaches.

On the plane back to Cincinnati, Big Mo suddenly went into a coma. When the plane landed, he was rushed to the hospital. At first the doctors were puzzled as to the cause of the coma. They didn't know of the tumble he had taken in the game with the Minneapolis Lakers, for that had happened three days earlier, and Stokes had apparently recovered. When the doctors were told of Mo's fall, they took X rays of his head. The X rays showed that the motor-control center of his brain was badly damaged.

Maurice Stokes was paralyzed. The doctors said he would be unable to move or talk for the rest of his life.

Jack Twyman and Maurice Stokes had never been the best of friends. They had been teammates and had enjoyed joking with each other, but that was about all. However, when Jack learned how badly Stokes had been injured, he went into action.

Stokes would have to remain in the hospital for many years—perhaps the rest of his life. Jack knew there wasn't enough money to pay for the doctors, nurses, medicine, and hospital room. So he convinced the NBA to stage a benefit game to raise money for his former teammate.

On October 21, 1958, the first Maurice Stokes benefit game was played. Some of basketball's greatest stars took part and even paid their way in. The game raised $10,000 for Big Mo.

Jack realized, however, that Stokes needed more than money. He needed the will to continue living. Jack frequently visited him at the hospital. At first, Jack did all the talking, but after a while they worked out a system so that Mo could respond. Jack would recite the alphabet, and when he came to the letter Stokes wanted to use, Mo would blink his eyes. They repeated this routine over and over, spelling out what Mo wanted to say. It was a long process, slow and painful, but at least Big Mo was communicating with his friend.

Slowly Mo began to learn how to talk again. He had to start from the beginning, first making sounds for the letters of the alphabet, then saying simple words like "cat" and "dog" and "yes." This, too, was a slow, slow process, but he refused to quit. Eventually he began to say more difficult words.

Mo worked hard and often strained to get the words out of his mouth. Jack stayed by his side, encouraging and prodding him to greater effort. Once Mo actually spit as he tried to say a tough word. Jack wiped his face and asked, "Hey, Mo, do you supply towels with your showers?"

Finally he began to say whole sentences. He said them slowly and with long pauses, but he said them. And Jack Twyman was there to joke with him, to tease him, and to keep Mo's spirits up.

"Hey, Mo, I was a better college player than you. Remember when we played against each other? I scored one point more in that game than you did."

"Jack . . ." gasped his friend, "you're . . . always . . . bragging . . . about . . . that. . . . I . . . wasn't . . . feeling . . . well . . . that . . . day."

Now that Mo could speak, he began therapy lessons to gain some small amount of movement. As a part of the therapy he learned to make ceramic objects, and they were good, too! Following another Maurice Stokes benefit game, Big Mo gave each player an ashtray or a vase to show his appreciation. But most of the ceramics went to Jack Twyman, who frequently joked about them, too.

"You sign these things with your initials, M. S. Who do you think you are—Picasso?"

Stokes grinned and replied, "Picasso . . . never . . . played . . . forward."

In 1967 Maurice Stokes attended one of his benefit games. A plane was hired to take him from Cincinnati to the town in New York State where the game was played. As he was wheeled out onto the court, the sellout crowd and the players stood and cheered. Mo's courage and fighting spirit had touched the hearts of thousands.

Maurice Stokes died in 1970. The Maurice Stokes benefit game is still held every year, but the money now goes to other worthy causes.

Jack Twyman had helped Stokes in his need, but Big Mo was not the only one to benefit. Twyman himself had gained quite a bit.

"You know," he said, "whenever I felt down in the dumps about something, I'd visit Mo. He always cheered me up. I've become a better person because of that man."

## Foul Shot

With two 60's stuck on the scoreboard
And two seconds hanging on the clock,
The solemn boy in the center of eyes,
Squeezed by silence,
Seeks out the line with his feet,
Soothes his hands along his uniform,
Gently drums the ball against the floor,
Then measures the waiting net,
Raises the ball on his right hand,
Balances it with his left,
Calms it with fingertips,
Breathes,
Crouches,
Waits,
And then through a stretching of stillness,
Nudges it upward.

The ball slides up and out,
Lands,
Leans,
Wobbles,
Wavers,
Hesitates,
Exasperates,
Plays it coy
Until every face begs with unsounding
                    screams—
And then

                    And then,

                              And then,

Right before ROAR-UP,
Dives down and through.

Edwin A. Hoey

182

# River of Peril

by Raboo Rodgers

The Company was transferring Ben's father to the city, to an apartment. The Company—big and impersonal—did not care about Brandy, Ben's Irish setter. It did not care that an eighty-pound purebred Irish setter could never be cooped up inside a four-room apartment. It did not care that Ben would have to give up Brandy, find him another home, within one week.

Brandy laid his head contentedly in Ben's lap, and Ben rubbed him behind the ears.

"I thought we might run an ad in the paper," Ben's father said. "There'll be a lot of people who would jump at the chance to own a fine setter like Brandy."

"Yeah," Ben mumbled, feeling his throat twist into a tight knot.

His father let the subject drop. "Tell you what," he said. "I've got a million things to do before we leave, and you and that dog are in my way. You might as well use the canoe one last time. Suppose I put you in upriver, and you two take your time floating down to Alpine?" He smiled warmly at his son, a smile that meant he understood what the boy was going through. He was offering Ben a final chance to be with his dog—an opportunity for them to say good-bye to each other privately. "What do you say?"

Ben nodded.

In three days his father would meet them at the bridge near the little settlement of Alpine, but now Ben and Brandy were alone. It was early morning, and the mist was beginning to lift from the quiet waters of the river. There were no rapids yet, but a soft whisper coming up the river indicated fast water a half mile away.

"Get up front," Ben told Brandy, and the gleaming, muscular Irish setter picked his way carefully over the gear and sat on his haunches in the bow of the canoe.

Ben dug his paddle into the water, and the canoe knifed downstream. With the gear stowed in the middle and Brandy's eighty pounds in the bow, the aluminum canoe was balanced well and handled easily.

The still water gradually began to move. A limb dangling in the river showed there was current, and the whisper of the first rapids became a muffled roar. Ben felt his heartbeat quicken.

When they were in the rapids, each stroke of the paddle had to be exact. Each maneuver had to be timed perfectly or the canoe might slip broadside against a rock, and the churning water would roll it, throwing boy and dog into the river to be battered and bruised against the rocks. Worse, the canoe could become wedged against one of the huge boulders that peppered the river. With tons of water pouring against it, the canoe would be immovable. Ben had once seen a canoe wedged so tightly that four strong men couldn't break it free. And he had seen canoes broken in half and wrapped around trees and boulders like strips of aluminum foil.

Between the rocks directly ahead was a straight line where the water suddenly dropped out of sight. On the other side of the line Ben could see spray shooting into the sky. And there was noise—noise rushing up the river to greet them.

Brandy got up on all fours, looked ahead, then back at Ben, and whined. "Down," Ben commanded, and Brandy stretched out in the bottom of the canoe with his head resting on the gunwale.

Ben slipped from the seat to his knees, to get the center of gravity as low as possible. He back paddled, taking a hard stroke on each side and killing the canoe's speed so he could plot his course through the shoal. The canoe hung there for a few seconds, and Ben saw where he would have to go.

The water fell quickly, ran straight for about thirty yards, washed up against a huge rock, and then rolled off to the left. Once he was in the current, Ben would have to draw for all he was worth to escape piling into the rock and being destroyed.

He back paddled another few strokes, maneuvering the canoe a few feet to the left and into a better position. Then it happened. The bow flew up over the falling water, dropped, and Ben was caught in the grip of the current. Desperately, he dug the paddle in. The rock loomed ahead, but the canoe responded to the paddle, and the bow swung away to the left. At the last instant, Ben drew in hard, heavy strokes to the left. The stern swung out to follow the bow and barely nicked the rock.

Ben back paddled and straightened the canoe. The pointed bow plunged down into the swirling, foaming water, and a wave broke over the gunwale, soaking both Brandy and Ben, and sloshing around in the bottom.

They were past the roughest part, and Ben skillfully threaded the canoe through the remaining rocks. They came out free and easy into calm, clear water.

Brandy made the canoe rock as he shook the water from his hair. Ben laughed and began bailing out the canoe. He could be more relaxed from now on.

When the sun was high overhead, he eased the canoe up to a small, shaded, gravel bar. After he and Brandy had eaten and rested, he swam in the cool water, with Brandy eagerly following. Brandy was an expert swimmer, strong and at home in the water.

There were thirty miles of river ahead of them. Ben knew he could cover that distance easily in three days, but he preferred to put a sizable stretch of it behind them now. He cut the swim short, and they shoved off.

By midafternoon he estimated they had covered about a dozen miles, enough for the first day, and he began to think about setting up camp. But first there was dinner to prepare. The idea of a couple of smallmouth bass lying side by side in a frying pan of hot fat made his mouth water. He got his spinning rod and reel and put on his favorite top-water lure.

The current was moving, but not too fast, and a few casts along the bank produced a brownie about twelve inches long. It gave Ben a good fight, dancing and leaping across the water. He pulled the brown bass into the canoe, and Brandy came back to inspect it, obviously not much impressed as it flopped around at his feet. Brandy gave Ben a rather indignant look and returned to the bow of the canoe.

"One more bass," Ben thought, "would be enough." He looked for a likely spot for another brownie and spied a small pocket just out of the current and recessed into the bank about ten feet. It was ringed with large rocks and a log that was partially submerged in the water. Ben was sure the granddaddy of all smallmouth bass would be holed up in there.

As the canoe drifted downstream, he made his cast. The line arched out over the water, and the lure sailed straight into the pocket—and right over the log where the hooks bit in and hung. Ben snatched at the line to free the lure, but the hooks sank deeper into the rotten wood.

Disgusted, Ben back paddled into the pocket hoping to free the lure. Then he made a disastrous mistake.

Without looking, he reached over the partially submerged log to free the lure. When he did look, it was too late. Lying coiled on a flat rock on the other side of the log was the biggest, meanest moccasin he had ever seen. In the split second before the snake struck, Ben saw how it had earned the name "cottonmouth." The inside of its mouth was as white as a ball of cotton.

The snake's head seemed as big as Ben's fist, its body as thick as his arm, and it seemed to strike from pure meanness. The head shot out, then snapped downward, sinking sharp fangs into the flesh just below Ben's wrist.

That was bad enough. But things got worse.

As the fangs were driven in, Ben snatched his hand away and pulled the cottonmouth with it. The snake fell into the canoe at Ben's feet and coiled again. Cotton-mouths are nervous and, unlike most snakes, will strike repeatedly.

There was nothing Ben could do. In desperation he leaped to his feet, intending to step on the snake's head. But the cottonmouth was faster.

As Ben kicked out at the snake, it struck again, sink-ing its fangs into the rubber toe of his sneaker, barely missing the flesh of his toes. Wildly, he shook the snake from his foot, but again it coiled, ready to strike.

Suddenly Ben saw a blur of red coming toward him like a freight train. Then he was knocked out of the canoe by the full force of Brandy's eighty pounds striking him in the chest.

He hit the shallow water off-balance, driving his foot at a sharp angle into a crack between two slick rocks. Then he felt the deep, searing pain burning his ankle.

Jerking his foot free of the rocks, Ben looked on in horror as the cottonmouth struck at Brandy. But the big setter leaped back just in time. Then, before the snake could coil again, the dog was on it, snarling with all the fury of a wild animal.

Ben could hear Brandy's jaws snapping together as the dog disappeared beneath the gunwale. Suddenly Brandy jerked his head up, and the thick moccasin was in his mouth, held in a firm grip behind its ugly head. Unable to twist and get its fangs into the setter, the snake coiled itself around Brandy's neck, but the big dog was unaffected. Snarling and baring his teeth, Brandy shook the cottonmouth like a rag, until finally it dropped with a thud to the bottom of the canoe.

Brandy stood motionless, watching the snake thrash and coil. Mouth open and fangs extended, it was still trying to bite. But now the cottonmouth was dead, and only its nerves were making it move. Brandy looked up at his master.

Ben was frozen, numb. His mind refused to accept what had happened. He stood in the water and looked at his dog looking at him. Then the fog cleared from his brain and he knew he had to get into action, or he would die.

Limping on the hot, burning ankle, he pulled the canoe to the bank and collapsed there as he tried to gather what was left of his wits.

*Snakebite!* His mind reeled as he recalled all he knew about the proper treatment. Tourniquets could be extremely dangerous. So could cutting into the fang marks and trying to suck out the venom.

Above all else, Ben knew that he shouldn't exert himself. But he simply had no other choice. He had to get out as much of the poison as he could and hope the exertion wouldn't pump what was left of it into his heart.

He would use a tourniquet briefly. He ripped the hem from the bottom of his T-shirt, wrapped it around his wrist, and twisted it tight with a stick.

Before he unsheathed his hunting knife, Ben looked at the snake's head. The poison sacs on each side had held a lot of venom, and he knew that most of that venom was now in the back of his hand.

He held the knife over the first fang mark. Then, gritting his teeth, he shoved the point down into the flesh. The blood poured briefly, then stopped because of the pressure of the tourniquet. Ignoring the pain, Ben cut into the other fang mark. He put his mouth over the fresh wounds and sucked and spit until he could get no more blood. Discarding the tourniquet, he let the cuts bleed freely for a few moments, then bandaged them tightly with another strip of his shirt to stop the bleeding. The swelling already had begun around the fang marks, and a sickening discoloration was spreading with the puffiness. Ben knew he had to get to a hospital.

He looked at his map. The river wound and twisted for seventeen more miles before reaching the Alpine bridge. The nearest highway was closer, only six miles away, but he would have to climb over the mountain and struggle through a tangle of brush to get to it. He knew that his ankle, already swollen and turning purple, would never hold up. He had no choice. Downriver was his only hope.

Hopping on one foot, he unloaded his camping gear and threw it on the bank. "Get up front," he said, and Brandy took his place in the canoe. Ben shoved off. Between his feet lay the moccasin. He dropped it into the river.

Ben checked his watch. Three or four hours of daylight were left. After that, he would be on the river in darkness and unable to maneuver through the rapids with any degree of safety. Fear stabbed deep into his chest. The odds against making it to Alpine were great. The seventeen miles loomed ahead like a thousand.

Ben took the first stroke with the paddle. His left hand was swollen and practically useless. His fingers were swollen, too. They hurt when he tried to curl them over the end of the paddle. He pulled the blade through the water with his right hand and then dragged it at the end of the stroke so he wouldn't have to change sides.

The first hour there was little current, and the canoe drifted slowly. When the rapids appeared, Ben was glad. He could make better time now.

"Down," he told Brandy, as he headed the canoe straight into the rolling water. It was an easy run. He held onto the paddle, making a rudder of it, and steered clear of the rocks. The river ran straight and wide over a shallow, gravel bottom, and all he had to do was to keep the bow pointed downstream and ride the swift current.

Ben's ankle was straight out in front of him, stiff, swollen, useless. The flesh ballooned to such a size that the anklebone was practically buried.

The sun dropped lower in the cloudless sky, but the heat seemed to grow more intense. Ben scooped water from the river and drank it. He splashed it over his face and neck, but that did little good. He wanted to get out of the life jacket, but he didn't dare. If he should be dumped by the rapids, he wouldn't be able to swim for long with only one arm and one leg.

His vision blurred, and he became ill. Holding onto the gunwale with his good hand, he leaned over the side of the boat. He had never been so sick in his life.

He lay back against the raised stern and let the canoe drift. "There is no use trying," he thought. "I'll never make it." Ben closed his eyes.

With the canoe drifting broadside down the river, Brandy knew something was wrong. Stepping carefully, he walked to the stern and put his cool, wet nose against his master's neck. Ben didn't respond.

The red setter opened his mouth and gripped Ben's good arm, his sharp teeth clamping down hard. Ben opened his eyes and laid his hand on the dog's broad head. "You don't want me to quit, do you?" he mumbled. Brandy quivered with excitement at hearing Ben's voice. "OK, you red mutt, get up front. We'll go on." Somehow Ben did.

Night came. The river became a dimly lit silver trail in the moonlight. When they ran rapids, Ben could not see the rocks until he was upon them. He kept the canoe as straight as possible and hoped they would be lucky. For a while, they were. However, the canoe took a terrific battering, bouncing off the rocks like a bumper car.

Ben grew weaker, exhausted. He wanted to sleep, and when they had bounced and banged their way through another set of rapids into a calmer stretch of water, he did. He leaned back, closed his eyes, and drifted off. The canoe floated downriver like a piece of debris.

He didn't know how far they had gone or how long he had been asleep, when the noise awakened him. Brandy was standing on the front seat barking as loud as he could, but Ben could hardly hear him. The noise of the rapids was drowning him out.

Ben's head felt heavy, and his throat was tight and dry. He grabbed the paddle and tried to back the canoe against the current with his one good hand. He couldn't. Ahead, the river sounded like a hundred freight trains.

In the moonlight he could see a line of rocks—huge, dark things against the sky. And he could see spray shooting into the air, a fountain twenty feet high.

Ben put his swollen hand on top of the paddle to steady his stroke, but the fingers refused to bend. His palm was so numb he couldn't feel the paddle.

He back paddled with one arm and got the canoe
straight, but it was useless to fight the current. "Down,"
he shouted to Brandy over the deafening roar. Then he
coaxed his injured ankle out farther and slid off the seat
into the bottom of the canoe, lowering the center of
gravity.

He gripped the paddle low, near the blade, and with
his arm over the gunwale, he used it as a rudder.

The river poured through a break in the rocks and
then disappeared into a hole of darkness. Below that was
where the spray was leaping into the air, where the noise
was coming from. Ben split the distance between the
rocks evenly.

One minute the canoe was on the water going between
the rocks; the next it was in the air, floating, falling. Ben

felt his stomach start climbing up his throat. The impact of the canoe hitting flat on the water sent sharp pains through his ankle and snapped his head against the gunwale, laying a two-inch gash over one eye.

Ben was stunned. In the darkness all he could see was water. Raging, foaming, it was everywhere—above him, below him, around him. The paddle was gone; he didn't even know when he had lost it. He looked toward the bow of the canoe and saw that Brandy was gone, too.

Up ahead was another group of rocks. The water ripped through them with uncontrolled fury. It piled into one large boulder, rocketed off another, roared down a narrow chute, and plowed into the base of a cliff. Ben saw his only chance. At that moment, his decision was made.

The canoe was half filled with water and about to roll. He leaned to one side, dumped the canoe, and fell into the water.

As he watched, the current spun the canoe around, sending it down the chute and tossing it from one rock to another. Above the roar of the water, he could hear the sickening cry of the metal as it was twisted and torn. The river fell more steeply, and the mangled canoe picked up speed.

It struck a rock, bow first, ten yards in front of the cliff. The canoe rode up over the rock and was tossed into the air, where it performed a neat half flip, half twist, leveled into a perfect layout, and slammed with tremendous force into the face of the cliff. Awed, Ben watched as the canoe, now a heap of scrap metal, fell back into the churning water and was washed away.

After it disappeared, Ben realized that he, too, was being carried with the current, toward the rocks. He didn't care. He wouldn't fight. He was too sick, too weak. He would accept the same fate as his canoe.

The current tore at his arms and legs, racking the injured muscles with pain. His hip slammed into a rock, but he already had so much pain he hardly felt the impact. His body began to spin downward. He was aware that his head was where his feet should have been, and he could feel his good leg flopping free in the air above him.

"It's almost over," he thought. He pictured the water shooting him toward the cliff, where he would be mangled like the canoe. Then he felt it, felt the air exploding from his lungs as his back struck the hard granite.

Upside down, under water, and pinned against the cliff, he was finished.

"No!" he suddenly thought. "No! I won't die. Not like this." He worked the foot of his good leg down the granite wall, and with more determination than strength, he shoved.

His head popped up, and he sucked in huge gulps of the cool night air. He opened his eyes; he was alive and drifting into calm water.

But he had no canoe. He could not walk. He could barely maneuver himself through the water. Blood was running out of the gash and into his eye. And worst of all, he was alone.

Ben could see out of only one eye now. The sight of the other eye was blurred. So when he saw the dark shape swimming toward him, he was afraid to hope. But it *was* Brandy! With powerful strokes that almost lifted his chest clear of the water, the dog swam to Ben.

Ben grabbed him, burying his face in the wet hair of Brandy's neck. Now he had a chance again. With his good hand he took a firm grip on the long, flowing tail. "Go ahead, Brandy," he said. "Go ahead."

The setter almost leaped out of the water and then began swimming with strong, steady strokes down the middle of the river, towing Ben behind him.

Ben's hand clung to Brandy's tail. Even when he lost consciousness, his hand kept its firm grip.

There were no more rapids.

When Ben opened his eyes again, the gray of dawn had already settled over the river. He had no idea where

they were or how much farther they had to go, but Brandy was towing him toward the bank.

Then Ben heard a wonderful noise—the click-clack of a car passing over an expansion joint. He looked up. The Alpine bridge was high over his head. They had made it! All he had to do was to get up to the highway and flag down a car.

But when Brandy pulled him to the bank, Ben found he could not stand. His swollen ankle looked horrible and was useless. His good leg was too weak and bruised to take his full weight. Grasping a willow bush with his good hand, he pulled himself out of the water. Brandy, near exhaustion now, stretched out on the ground and anxiously watched his master struggle onto the bank.

Overgrown with weeds and scrub brush, the ground sloped fifty yards up to the highway. On one knee and one elbow Ben started crawling. Briars tore at his arms and legs. Another car click-clacked across the expansion joint of the bridge and continued on down the highway.

Ten yards from the shoulder of the road, Ben collapsed flat-out in the weeds. Brandy nuzzled him, whined, danced anxiously in front of him. But Ben could go no farther.

Another car passed, so close that Ben could see the top of the windows and the roof. But he could not crawl one more inch toward the highway.

Brandy sat down by Ben and licked his face lovingly, encouragingly. "It was a good try, Brandy," Ben whispered. "This is as close as we could have come without making it."

The big setter's ears perked up, and he dashed to the highway. Ben heard the sound of an approaching car, and

Brandy's frantic barking. He heard the car cross the bridge, and he heard the screech of the tires on the pavement as the driver locked his brakes. Then an angry voice shouted at Brandy, and the car roared away.

Brandy came back to Ben. "It's OK, boy," Ben told him. "You've done all you can."

But the muscular setter had one trick left. Clamping his strong jaws to the top of the life vest behind Ben's neck, and crouching and stiffening his legs, Brandy began to drag Ben through the weeds. Jerking and pulling, an inch or two at a time, the determined dog edged Ben ever closer to the road. He snorted. He strained. He pulled. He dragged Ben's face through the briars. He ripped off a piece of the life vest, took another grip, and continued pulling.

Again a car came across the bridge. It slowed, stopped. Ben heard the voices of two men discussing what the dog might have in the weeds. He heard a door open and close. Another. Footsteps crunched on the gravel shoulder. One of the men exclaimed, and Ben felt hands rolling him over.

He looked up into the man's face. His throat was too dry to speak. All he could do was smile. His eyes filled with tears, and the tears ran down his face.

It was against all the rules. Dogs were not allowed in hospitals. They said it was against the law to have dogs in hospitals. But, try as they did, the nurses, attendants, doctors—none of them—could keep Brandy out.

They would take him outside, and he would dash back in the next time a door was opened. Instinctively, he could find his way down the long halls, up the stairs, and into Ben's room.

Finally, they gave up and let him stay under Ben's bed, pretending he wasn't there, so no one could be accused of knowingly breaking the rules. But when the nurses brought Ben his meals, there was always an unexplained dish of scraps from the kitchen. And when they came back and the dish was empty, they just smiled.

A newspaper reporter came, and Ben got Brandy out from under the bed long enough to have his picture taken.

The swelling went down in Ben's arm and ankle. The cut over his eye was neatly stitched and the doctors said there would be only a tiny scar.

Now everything was fine.

Everything except the one thing that really mattered.

When Ben got out of the hospital, he and his father would be moving to the city. And Brandy would be left behind.

"Isn't there any way we could take him with us?" Ben asked his father, almost pleading. "Couldn't we keep him in the apartment?"

"Would you really prefer that?" his father asked. "Would you want him cooped up in an apartment with no place to run?"

Ben didn't have to answer. He laid his head back on the pillow and tried to shut his mind to the fact that

Brandy, who had saved his life, had to be given away. Brandy squirmed out from under the bed and rested his head close to Ben. Ben's hand went behind the setter's ears. Ben's father shook his head sadly and left.

But when he returned the next day, he was smiling. And that angered Ben a little. Then his father quit smiling and began to grin. To Ben it seemed cruel that his father could be in such high spirits, when Ben's whole world was collapsing around him.

From his pocket Ben's father pulled a yellow paper, a telegram. "From the president of the Company, Ben," he said. "He read about you and Brandy in the newspaper. I've never met the man. I barely know his name."

"What's he say?" Ben asked, not sure what to think about a man in New York, whose decisions could affect thousands of people.

His father answered slowly, letting the full impact of his words fill the tiny hospital room. "He says that when we get to the city, there'll be a house waiting for us—a house with a big yard and all the room Brandy will ever need."

Had Ben been standing, his knees would have given way from pure joy. "You hear that Brandy? You hear that, boy?" he said, leaning his head over the rail of the hospital bed. "You get to stay, you hound. Nobody's gonna give you away—ever!"

Even Brandy seemed to sense the impact of the telegram. He crawled out from under the bed and leaped right onto the middle of it. He licked Ben's face and pulled playfully at his hospital gown.

There were paw prints all over the clean, white sheets, but no one cared.

# Whitewater Challenge

by Peter B. Mohn

THUNK! went the red fiberglass kayak on a rock hidden under the water.

The kayaker worked furiously with the paddle to get away from the rock.

The kayak backed off a little. Then the rushing current took the rear end of the kayak and pushed it around so the boat was going sideways downstream.

The kayaker dug furiously with the paddle, trying to point the boat downstream again. With a last desperate stroke, the kayaker lost balance, and the boat tipped over.

Quickly and efficiently the kayaker completed an Eskimo roll. With one strong stroke of the paddle the fiberglass boat was turned from upside down to right side up.

Maneuvering a kayak through turbulent whitewater, or the rapids of a river, is a fascinating sport, but it is not without danger. A few safety measures must be taken. This is why most kayakers wear helmets to protect their heads from rocks in case they capsize. And all of them wear life jackets.

Most kayakers are careful people. They do not rush into whitewater without knowing ahead of time the kind of rapids they will find. If there is any question, they may stop upstream, get out of the boat, and "scout" the river from dry land. They may decide to portage around the rapids and then try the whitewater farther downstream. The kayaker who prepares for danger enjoys the sport. The one who doesn't may get hurt.

Once in the rapids a boat must be kept upright so it will not capsize. The bow must be pointed downstream at all times. The kayaker must work hard to keep the boat moving fast. Otherwise the current will take over. When

that happens, the boat will be turned sideways and possibly slammed against a rock. It may be bent double, and it will likely capsize.

Kayaks are not the only boats that can be paddled through whitewater. Canoes can also be used. Two people in a canoe can help each other. When going downstream, the bow paddler can tell the stern paddler where to steer

so the boat will not crash into dangerous rocks. A canoe is light and easy to portage around rapids.

Whitewater fun is not limited to boats. An inner tube can provide hours of enjoyment in a stream that is not too deep for a person to touch bottom. Such streams are generally slower moving, so the danger in whitewater is less. All that is really needed is a bathing suit. A light jacket, however, could keep one from getting a bad case of sunburn.

A person simply climbs into the middle of an inner tube and pushes off. Paddling is possible but not necessary. Since the tube is round, it can float downstream in any direction—headfirst or feetfirst.

Rafts provide whitewater fun on some of the great rivers of the West. For many years only a few people dared to take their canoes through the turbulent waters of the canyons. Today guides take groups of people through on rafts.

Most of these trips begin in quiet water. The scenery is beautiful. The canyon walls glow with many soft colors.

The raft drifts leisurely along as the guide describes the history of the area.

Then suddenly the river turns white and wild. The rubber raft tosses and bends. Water pours in from all sides.

The guide pulls against the oars to keep from slamming into the rocks and canyon walls. At times the raft seems to be going uphill in the downhill river, flying over rocks hidden beneath the surface. Then almost as suddenly as it plunged into the rapids, the raft drifts into quiet water.

That's what canyon trips are like—moments of sun-filled peace, watching scenery and wildlife, followed by sudden plunges into the surging current.

Whitewater fun is an exciting leisure-time activity. It is not limited to the most daring kayakers or canoeists. It can be enjoyed by anyone who loves the challenge of a fast-moving current.

## The Dive

One moment, poised above the flashing blue:
The next I'm slipping, sliding through
The water that caresses, yields, resists,
Wrapping my sight in cooling grey-green mists.
Another moment—and I swirl, I rise,
Shaking the water from my blinded eyes,
And strike out strong, glad that I am alive,
To swing back to the grey old pile from which I dive.

Cornelia Brownell Gould

# Skiing Is Believing

by Linda Joseph

Skiing is a rapidly growing sport. Even so, most of the people in this country do not know how to ski. The strength and coordination that the sport demands, as well as its possible danger, discourage many Americans from taking to the slopes. Yet absurd as it may seem, hundreds of blind adults and children are learning to ski. This is due to a program called Blind Outdoor Leisure Development, or BOLD.

The skiers shown in the photographs are not necessarily those mentioned in the selection.

Not long ago, the Los Angeles chapter of BOLD participated in a five-day blind skiers' clinic given free of charge at the Kirkwood Ski Area in the California High Sierras. Chapter member Lorita Betraun, 22, attended the clinic. She says she was terribly frightened the first time she made a run.

"It reminded me of flying, and it was scary," she explains. "The first time I made a run without any contact with my instructor, I felt I was going so fast that I didn't know what might happen. It was like taking a fast plunge in a high-speed elevator. You know that feeling, like your heart is in your mouth."

Yet after overcoming their initial fears, the BOLD skiers became quite excited about their newfound sport. As with sighted skiers, their coordination improved with experience.

Dora Nova, 21, another member of BOLD, explains her enthusiasm for the sport. "It's an incredible feeling of freedom, motion, and joy," she says. "It just blows my mind when I think about it. What's really fantastic is you don't have to see to ski."

Indeed, thanks to techniques developed in 1969 at Aspen, Colorado, the blind can be taught to participate in a sport that at one time seemed limited to sighted people. The unique method that has made this possible links the ski instructor to the blind pupil with a 12-foot bamboo pole. The blind pupil is not allowed to ski alone until the instructor believes the pupil is able to do so.

It was 1969 when Jean Eymere, a former member of the French Olympic skiing team, lost his sight due to an illness. His fellow instructors in Aspen used him as a guinea pig while trying to discover the best method for teaching the blind how to ski. They tried using beepers, poles, and radios. Finally they decided that a guide who was constantly talking and giving encouragement was the best kind of help.

Eymere, who helped establish BOLD and is still one of its strongest members, believes that skiing is the most unique, exciting thing blind people can do. If they can ski, he believes they can do almost anything else.

"BOLD has taken some blind pupils who had never skied before all the way to the most advanced turns," he says. "But how well they ski is not as important as the fact that they are getting turned on to something new. They are doing something unique, something outlandish, something absurd for a blind person."

Pam March, a Kirkwood ski instructor, says, "Blind skiers are easier to teach than the sighted skiers. They are not as easily distracted on the slopes.

"Some techniques used with blind skiers are very much like those used with sighted skiers," Pam explains. "Verbal communication is constant. As the 'eyes' of the pupil, the instructor is continually locating her own and her pupil's position.

"Ski instructors are not only responsible for the training of a blind skier—they are also responsible for the skier's life. They must know where the skier is going at all times and who or what is coming near. When no definite instructions are being given to the blind pupil, the instructor constantly repeats the verbal command 'Go! Go! Go!'

"Signs are used on the slopes, advising everyone that blind skiers are present. Each pupil wears a bib marked 'BLIND SKIER.' The instructors wear bright-colored jackets. Above all, the instructors know what each pupil is capable of doing—and stay within those limits."

Dora Nova laughs as she describes one of her moments at Kirkwood. "On Lift Number One for beginners, the slope drops off quite rapidly on the right side. And if you're not ready for it—wow! My instructor and I were free skiing when he told me to stop. The stopping point was directly on the edge of this drop-off. He stopped and I tried. But my skis picked up speed.

"I sat down on my rear end, and my skis just kept running until they encountered this heavy bush. By the time my instructor got to me, I was thoroughly wrapped up in the bush. He couldn't tell which limbs belonged to me and which belonged to the bush."

Lorita Betraun outdid her friend by getting her skis tangled up and falling out of the double chairlift. This happens even to the most advanced skiers. A well-known racing champion fell out of a chairlift twice in one season! And Dandy Don Meredith, the quarterback turned sportscaster turned actor, dislocated his shoulder while boarding a chairlift at Aspen a few seasons back.

"It was no big deal when I tumbled out of the chair," Lorita remembers. "Though I had the wind knocked out of me, I wasn't hurt. But some of the others were shook. You would have thought I was an important movie star the way they fussed over me. That part was nice."

Lorita's most exciting moment was when she skied Lift Number Six at Kirkwood. Number Six is a long run bordered on both sides by a grove of evergreen trees.

"My instructor and I must have looked like a pair of dancers on skis. That's because I was so scared of this run that I wrapped my arms around his waist and held on for dear life. And when it was over, I sat right down in the snow and didn't move for half an hour. It took me that long to recover. Then we rode the chairlift back up, and I conquered that run on my own."

Dora finds that skiing is overcoming another barrier. "We are doing something most people said we couldn't do. And it has changed my inner self, too. It has increased my independence and made me a freer, happier person. After skiing, I'm ready to try anything."

Lorita has also found that skiing lessons have taught her more than how to master a difficult ski run.

"The goal for all blind skiers is more freedom. You don't have to see where you're going, as long as you go. In skiing, you ski with your legs and not with your eyes. In life, you experience things with your mind and your body. And if you're lacking one of the five senses, you adapt. Thanks to skiing and Kirkwood, are we ever learning to adapt!"

# Ocean-Born Mary

by Joseph Raskin and Edith Raskin

Whenever Ocean-Born Mary was asked by her American neighbors what her native land was, she would reply with a mysterious smile, "My parents came from Scotland; that much is certain." And when pressed to tell how she got her unusual name, she would reply vaguely, "Ah, that's a long story." When she was in the mood to tell it, her neighbors found it a remarkable story indeed.

Her father, James Wilson, had been a handsome man, as carefree as a colt let loose in the field. While the young people in the Scottish village were amused by his pranks, the older folks grumbled, "That lad'll come to no good." They raised their eyebrows in disbelief when they heard he was going to marry Elizabeth Fulton. "A pity—such a fine girl making such a sorry choice," they said.

None of this talk discouraged James and Elizabeth from marrying. Because it was not in James's nature to work steadily, life for Elizabeth was far from easy, but she did not complain.

One day James came home greatly excited. "I just met an Irish fellow," he said to his young bride. "He told me wonderful things about Ireland. We're going there! There's really no future for us in this desolate village."

James had a gift for words, and before long Elizabeth was just as eager to move to Ireland as he was. A month later, carrying their few belongings, they stepped onto the misty shore of North Ireland. Very soon, however, they discovered that this land was even more desolate than Scotland, and work was harder to get.

"Many people from around here are migrating to America," James told his disappointed wife. "They say all kinds of riches and land are there for the taking. We are going to America, too!"

Elizabeth also had been hearing fantastic tales about the New World. "We must leave here," she agreed. Then she added, a bit frightened, "But would it be safe for me to take such a long voyage?"

"Don't worry, it'll only take a few weeks to cross the ocean," James assured her.

When they boarded the four-masted ship, they found it was loaded with emigrants who, like themselves, were

221

looking forward to a happier life in the New World. At the same time Elizabeth couldn't help feeling sadness as she watched the shore of the Old World disappearing. "We may never see it again," she told her husband.

But James waved that off. "There's no need to be so sentimental."

It was a fine summer day, and as the ship plowed its way through calm waters into the open sea he said soothingly, "Looks as if we'll have a pleasant voyage."

"I hope so," Elizabeth replied.

For a week the sea stayed calm, and the fluffy little clouds floating in the sky offered no threat. But then heavy clouds appeared on the horizon and, as they covered the sky, spread gloom over the sea. The wind increased, whipping up huge waves and tossing the ship as though playing with it. The creaking and groaning of the ship and the roar of the sea sent terror into the passengers. Huddled together below deck, all they could do was pray for their safety. But toward morning the changing wind tore apart the solid blanket of clouds, the sea began to calm down, and cheerfulness again returned to those aboard the ship.

"The worst is over. The captain is promising smooth sailing from now on," James said soothingly to his wife. "Just the same, you'd better stay in bed."

The captain kept his promise. Day after day passed uneventfully, and there was nothing, not even the sight of a lone bird, to break the sameness of the voyage.

One morning James and some other passengers were standing on deck, talking about life aboard ship and wondering when they would reach shore. They had been sailing nearly three weeks and had barely gone halfway.

"A ship!" they suddenly heard the lookout shouting. It took a while before the morning fog lifted enough for them to spot a strange ship sailing directly toward them. As it came nearer, they could clearly see its menacing black flag. A pirate ship!

The frightening news spread quickly. Frantically, the passengers crowded around the captain, pleading that he do something to save them.

"Give us muskets, and we'll fight them off!" James demanded.

"We have no ammunition of any kind to speak of," replied the captain. "And without ammunition, there is nothing we can do but submit to whatever they may demand and hope they will spare our ship."

With a sense of approaching doom the emigrants watched the pirate ship closing in on them. They heard a trumpet blast from the pirates and the captain shouting back his willingness to submit to their demands. For a while it looked as though the outlaw ship, not heeding the captain's shouts, was moving headlong at them. They were somewhat relieved when at the last moment it suddenly came about and dropped anchor a short distance away.

The relief did not last long, however. Lowering their boats, the villainous pirates quickly reached the helpless ship and with amazing swiftness climbed up the ropes and onto the deck. With lightning speed they fell upon the crew and passengers, tying them hand and foot, then left them where they had fallen. The pirates would deal with their prisoners later.

The pirate captain, a fierce-looking, black-bearded giant, wearing high boots and a bright kerchief, urged them on. "Lively, my lads, round up the spoils!"

The pirates scattered about the ship, grabbing whatever booty they could find and piling it up on the deck for later transfer to their own ship.

Not satisfied with the haul his comrades had gathered, the pirate captain hurried below to the officers' quarters, hoping he would find the richest booty there. Knowing that all the officers were bound on deck, he did not expect to meet anyone. But when he flung open the door of a cabin, he stopped as though struck dumb. Bewildered, he regarded the sight before him. For there, lying in bed, was a woman with a baby at her side.

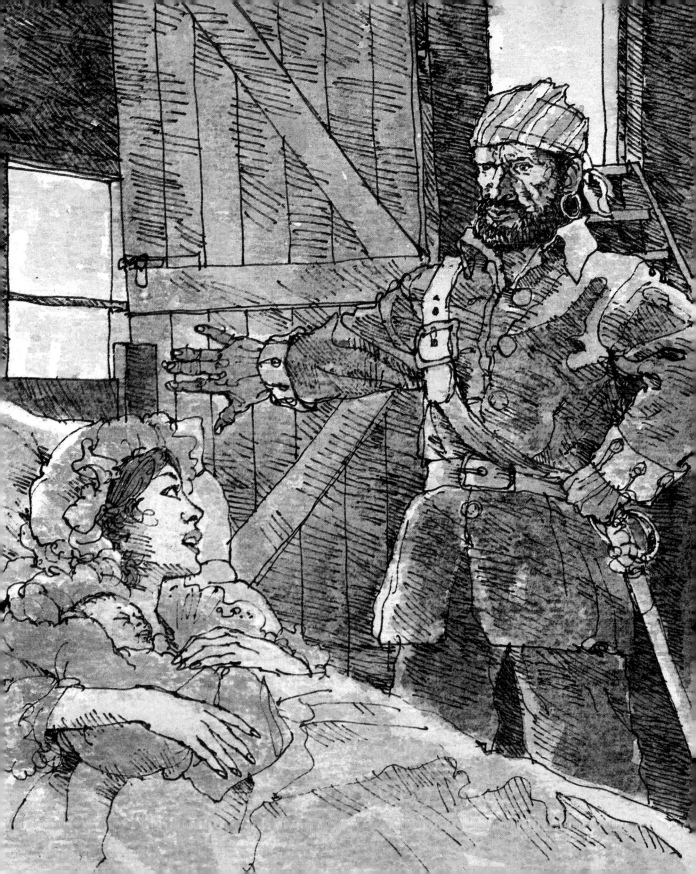

For a long moment the pirate stood gazing at the mother and child, uncertain what to do. "Why are you not on deck?" he demanded.

Frightened by his threatening voice and menacing appearance, the mother replied weakly, "I am not yet strong enough to walk."

"How old is your baby?"

"Two days."

"A girl?"

Now sensing kindness in his voice, she became more at ease. "Yes," she replied.

"Have you given her a name?"

"Not yet."

A tender smile, totally foreign to such a rugged man, lit up his face. "That's fine," he said. Stepping out of the cabin, he shouted to his men on deck, "Stop plundering and wait until I come up. Hear me!"

"Ay, ay!" came the response.

Satisfied that his order was being obeyed, he returned to the cabin. Then, quietly, so as not to disturb the sleeping baby, he tiptoed over to take a closer look. As if in a trance, he gazed at her steadily, and when he touched the tiny fingers, tears filled his eyes.

At last turning away from the child, he asked the mother, "What is your name?"

"Elizabeth Wilson," she replied. "We're on our way from Scotland to America."

"Listen carefully, Elizabeth," the pirate said. "If you let me name this little girl after another I once knew, I promise that you and all the passengers on the ship will be released and be allowed to sail on undisturbed. What do you say?"

Elizabeth regarded him with astonishment. At the same time she couldn't help feeling strangely sorry for this feared robber of the sea. Had the sight of her and her baby brought back sentimental memories of the past when he, too, had a wife and child dear to him?

"I agree," she said.

As he bent down over her and the baby, she heard him whisper, "Mary—beautiful Mary." She wondered if that had been his wife's name. But, before she could gather enough courage to ask, he was gone.

A few minutes later the passengers on deck heard something they hardly expected. "Untie the prisoners and give them back their belongings!" the pirate captain ordered, and his comrades meekly responded, "Ay, ay!"

After the sea robbers had finished undoing their villainous work, their captain shouted, "Now get under way, the lot of you!"

With astonishment the emigrants watched the pirates depart the ship. "What happened? Why did they change their minds?" they asked one another.

Suddenly the relief on deck erupted with everyone shouting, dancing, and congratulating one another on their surprising release.

However, the dancing and congratulations soon ended. The dreaded captain of the pirates had returned. He was alone. "What is he up to now?" they whispered, as they watched him heading for the officers' cabins, a large package under his arm.

Like the other passengers, Elizabeth was surprised to see the pirate captain back again. She gasped when he opened the package and unfolded a length of the most beautiful brocaded silk she had ever seen.

"For Mary. I want her to make a wedding gown from it," he said, placing the cloth beside the sleeping baby. Then, giving the child a last look, he quickly departed.

Crowding at the rails, the emigrants watched as the pirates lowered the black flag, set sail, and gradually disappeared in the distant fog.

Elizabeth's remarkable pact with the pirate captain soon became known to everyone on the ship. "You aren't really going to keep that promise?" they teased her.

"Yes, I am," Elizabeth replied firmly.

So the little girl was nicknamed Ocean-Born Mary, and the name remained with her all her life.

In spite of their anxieties, the emigrants met with no further trouble during the rest of the passage. It was in August, 1720, after eight weeks on the sea, that they happily sighted the shores of the New World and landed in Boston.

However, soon after their arrival, James Wilson became ill and died. Eventually, his widow, Elizabeth, married James Clark, and they settled in Londonderry, New Hampshire. Many years later one of their descendants, Horace Greeley, became a famous American writer.

But it was Ocean-Born Mary who was to be remembered most curiously. From a pretty little baby born aboard a ship in mid-ocean, she grew into a beautiful woman, tall and fair. When she was married on her eighteenth birthday, she wore a wedding gown which was made of the finest brocaded silk the people of Londonderry, New Hampshire, had ever seen.

This splendid wedding gown was handed down from generation to generation. And whenever Ocean-Born Mary's offspring gathered around the fireplace, they liked nothing better than to retell the tale of how a tiny baby helped to save a shipful of emigrants on the way to America.

# TRAIL BOSS IN PIGTAILS

by Marjorie Filley Stover

*Pa wasn't going to get well! Watching him, Emma Jane was suddenly sure of it. The long trip to Texas from Illinois three years earlier and the hot dry Texas climate had not made Pa better. And soon Emma Jane knew that Pa knew it, too. He knew it and had made a plan. The Burke family were going back to Illinois, back to where they had relatives. More than that, they were going to drive a herd of longhorn steers from Waco clear up to Chicago. The price the cattle would bring there would buy a farm for the family to live on.*

*So one early spring day the whole family set out with eighty-two head of cattle and Emma Jane as trail boss of the herd. Pa and the whole family were counting on her to bring the animals through. But even Pa, who didn't live through the journey, hadn't counted on all the problems they would meet. Emma Jane's resourcefulness was tested again and again.*

Emma Jane stirred in her bedroll and clung to its warmth for a few more precious minutes. She could hear Ma stirring outside and the breakfast fire crackling. Emma Jane sat up and fished for her boots in the half darkness of the tent. The other children were not stirring yet. She spooled her bedroll, quickly brushing off any grass that stuck to it. Then she thrust a loop of rope around it, and pulling it tight with a quick hitch, ducked out of the tent and stowed it in the wagon. Her bed was made.

"Mornin', Ma." Emma Jane sloshed a little water into the washbasin from the water barrel on the side of the wagon.

Ma greased the bake oven with bacon fat and began to slide in the little balls of biscuit dough. "Mornin', Emma Jane. Going to be a nice day."

"We can use a little sunshine after two days of rain—and with all that rain, I'm afraid the river's going to be up." Emma Jane hooked up the milk pail and headed for Daisy, who was staked nearby. Squatting down beside the cow, Emma Jane sent two white jets of milk singing into the bottom of the pail.

By the time the milking was finished, the little camp was buzzing with activity. The tent flaps were pulled back, and Easter was helping Phoebe spool her bedroll. Martha stumbled toward the wagon, barely able to see over her bedroll, which Easter had plopped into her outstretched arms.

Matt had dumped his roll by the wagon step and squirreled up onto the seat. His sharp eye spied a lizard darting through the grass, and he swooped down to chase it. Heedless of all else, he dived in front of Martha and slithered under the wagon after his prey.

Martha shrieked, swayed, and came tumbling down. "Matthew Burke," she shouted indignantly, "don't you ever look where you're goin'?"

"Let's get the tent down," called Emma Jane.

Emma Jane piled her tin plate with fried side meat and sourdough biscuits. She partially filled her cup with a dipper of fresh milk and then poured a stream of steaming black coffee until brown bubbles foamed about the rim. She ate her breakfast in hurried mouthfuls, stuffed a couple of extra biscuits into her pocket, and shoved her tin plate, cup, and eating irons into the waiting kettle of hot water.

Emma Jane let the cattle drift in the direction of the trail. She could see the hustle-bustle of breaking camp. The dishwater was poured over the dying fire. Matt, Phoebe, and Martha scooted back and forth carrying things to Ma, who packed them in the wagon.

Martin brought up the oxen one at a time and stood them in place so they could be hitched to the wagon. He helped Ma with the heavy yoke and lifted the bow up under Pete's throat and pushed the ends through the holes in the yoke. Then he slid the wooden bow pin through one end of the bow to hold it. Ma was pushing the other bow under Pepper's throat and fastening it with its bow pin. The yoke was chained to the wagon tongue.

Easter mounted Fanny and rode off to help Emma Jane. Easter did not like to herd. She would rather sit in the wagon and tat. But this was Martin's chance to crawl inside for a nap.

Ma cracked the whip, and Pete and Pepper strained forward. Nothing happened. Emma Jane, hanging back from the herd, was afraid that the heavy wagon was stuck in the soft, damp earth. But the oxen heaved harder, and the wagon lurched forward. Once more the Burke family were on their way.

Emma Jane relaxed in the saddle. Mules might be faster, she thought, but the oxen were powerful heavers; and when the ground was soft, their split hooves pulled out of the mud easier than mules.

The sun climbed higher in the sky, rapidly drying the ground. Nothing warmed up faster than a Texas morning. It was easy herding on the prairie. Flat as a person's hand the land stretched, now and again rising in a gentle swell or dipping to the brighter green of a watercourse.

By four in the afternoon they were outside Preston Bend, a thriving village because of the Red River and its Rock Bluff Crossing nearby. But as Emma Jane had feared, the river had spilled over its banks. They must set up camp till the river went down.

A week dragged by. From the rocky bluff, Emma Jane gazed across the turbulent waters and moodily traced a pattern with her forefinger on Star's neck. The water was down some; but the low, gentle slope on the other side, which made it easy for the cattle to come out, was still licked by the flood. Emma Jane was itchy to be on the move again.

She thought of the spunky remark she'd made several weeks earlier—that if the rivers flooded, all they'd have to do would be to make camp and wait for the water to go down. Well, they were waiting. Once again she measured the distance with her eye, and her fingers drummed on the saddle pommel as she studied the rampaging river. The Preston Bend ferry was operating, lessening the backed-up traffic, but to swim a herd——

A horse reined up beside her. In the saddle sat a man with a fiery red beard and a matching thatch of hair bristling from beneath his broad-brimmed hat. He gave a low whistle. "The Red's big swimming, I see."

Emma Jane flicked the ends of the reins across her open palm. "Been that way the past week. Rains up the river keeping it full, I reckon."

The man pushed back his hat and studied the sky. "'Pears to me we may git a few more bucketfuls tonight."

"Could be." Emma Jane snapped the leather ends of the reins so hard that they reddened her palm, but she didn't notice.

The man pulled his hat down again and went on talking, more to himself than to Emma Jane. "If the Red floods its banks again, there's no tellin' how long we might have to squat here waitin' to push across."

"Nothin' else to do," Emma Jane's voice was flat.

The newcomer rubbed his red beard and sucked thoughtfully on his lips. "River's full, but I've been across worse."

The restless flicking of the reins stopped. Emma Jane gazed squarely at man and horse in alert appraisal. "You aimin' to swim a herd across, Mister?"

"Yep. Got seven hundred critters comin' up the trail an hour behind me."

Emma Jane didn't wait to think twice. "If you're aimin' to cross, Mister, would you let us crowd our herd of eighty-two longhorns in behind yours? We'd sure like to get travelin' again."

"*Your* herd?" Bushy red eyebrows lifted in surprise.

"Yes, sir. Our whole family is goin' back to Illinois. We aim to sell our herd in Chicago."

Blue eyes appraised her sharply for a moment. "Oh— those your cattle I saw a couple of kids herdin' back aways?"

"I reckon."

The bushy brows pulled together. "Well, I can't see as there'd be any harm shovin' your critters in behind mine—long as you've got a good hand followin' 'em. That river's not gonna be any child's play. Tell your pa he's welcome to try the big swim if he wants—but he better have someone waitin' on t'other side to help cut 'em out.''

Emma Jane's eyes gleamed. "Thanks, Mister. Thanks a heap! I know—uh—Pa—uh, we'll have to break camp, but we'll be there. Just tell your drag man to be watchin' for us." With a kick of her heels and a wave of her hand, Emma Jane wheeled Star and galloped off.

"And I know it's just what Pa'd want," she told herself. "Pa said he knew I could do it, and I can."

She stopped by the herd to get Martin. He would have to be on the other side to help her. They left Easter with the longhorns and drove Pete and Pepper and Daisy ahead of them in an unwilling trot.

Emma Jane planned as they rode. "Daisy is a family cow, and she'll have to go on the ferry with the family. The river's too wild for her. You'll have to get some money from Ma for the ferry. Then hightail it to the landing as fast as you can. Alone on horseback you ought to make the next boat."

Martha and Phoebe were playing under an oak tree with their corncob dolls and a set of acorn cups and saucers when Martha looked up and saw them coming with the oxen. She jumped up, sending the acorn cups tumbling. "Has the Red gone down? Are we leaving?"

Phoebe took her cue from Martha and jumped up, too.

Matt abandoned the lizard he was chasing. "Are we goin'? Are we goin'?"

"We're leaving Texas," said Emma Jane, as Ma hurried from the tent. Even while Emma Jane's excited words spilled out the story, Ma was reaching into an inner skirt pocket for the black leather purse.

"Wait a minute, don't go yet," she told Martin as she handed him a coin. "You'll need a packet of food."

Emma Jane organized the children. She and Martha spooled the bedrolls, while Matt and Phoebe carried them to the wagon.

Emma Jane pulled a rope tight around a bedroll. "The man says we can just drive our cattle right in behind his, and it won't be any extra trouble at all to get them across, Ma. Ours is such a small herd."

Ma was stuffing corn pone and dried beef into a clean sack. "It'll be good to get goin' again. Here, Martin—be careful now." Mid hustle and bustle they waved him off.

Camp was nearly broken. Ma was yoking the oxen when Emma Jane swung into the saddle.

Ma shoved a bow pin into place. "You and Easter come on soon as you're sure the cattle are making it across with no trouble."

Emma Jane waved to show Ma that she had heard. She was only too well aware that Ma was under the impression the cowboys from the other herd were going to swim the Burke cattle across for them, and she was thankful Ma had been too rushed to have time to wonder about it.

She was also aware that the red-bearded trail boss had assumed that the man of the family would be there to swim after the herd. Right now she didn't want to enlighten either one of them. She had faith that Star could swim any river that any other horse could swim, and if Star could swim the big Red, she reckoned she could make it on Star's back.

By the time Emma Jane joined Easter, she could hear the bellowing of the approaching herd. She purposely kept her own cattle back from the trail. It would be better, she figured, if she did not talk to that trail boss again on this side of the river. She saw him riding point, his red beard flaming over his brown shirt. When he spotted her, he gave a signal. She responded and looked off toward camp, shading her eyes as if watching for someone. Almost at once she turned back and waved, indicating that the Burke cattle were ready to join the drag of his herd.

The trail boss rode on, pushing his steers along. It was easier to keep them from balking at the water's edge if they were carried into the river by the force of their own momentum.

Emma Jane and Easter watched until the drag came into view. Then they turned their longhorns toward the trail and swung in at the tail of the big herd.

A lanky cowboy, riding drag, blinked at the girls from under sandy lashes. His crooked teeth flashed. "Thought your trail boss was going to follow 'em across."

Emma Jane leaned forward and pretended to pull a cocklebur from Star's mane. "Sure thing. Everything's all set. We're still half a mile from the riverbanks."

The cowboy shrugged. Plenty of time for the trail boss of this pint-sized herd to join them. He turned back to his own cattle, assuming that some man in the girls' family would show up.

Emma Jane straightened in the saddle. Her spirits soared in relief. Across the tossing horns, she saw Easter staring at her with open mouth. Emma Jane set her lips in the determined way the Burke family knew so well. "What can I do about it, if *that's* what he thinks?"

Easter grinned.

As they neared the edge of the bluff, the girls could see the leaders of the herd swimming across. Only their heads were out of the water, and their great horns rocked gently back and forth like so many rocking chairs upon the water. The succeeding waves of closely packed bellowing animals stepped into the surging flood, following their leaders.

Down between the sides of the rocky chute went the Burke eighty-two.

Emma Jane had counted on the fact that the cowboys ahead would be too busy watching their own cattle to pay any attention to her, and she was right.

The lanky cowboy at the drag glanced back just before he shoved in the last of his steers. But even though he saw no trail boss, he had no time to question now. After all, it made no difference to him whether or not this pint-sized herd crossed the river. If their trail boss was late, he'd missed his chance.

Emma Jane watched anxiously. With a snort, Colonel plunged into the muddy river and the others followed— all except Patches. Together, Emma Jane and Easter forced the reluctant Patches in. Then Star was in the water. Emma Jane gave her an encouraging pat. "Atta girl, you can make it."

Easter's quivering voice followed them. "Good luck, good luck!"

The water was colder than Emma Jane had expected, and swifter as they neared the middle of the channel. Much swifter. Once the lanky cowboy looked back. She caught his amazed look, and thought she heard him groan. But she was too busy to be sure. She mustn't let Patches decide to turn around in the middle of the Big Red.

Star swam like an expert, steadily and strongly. Emma Jane watched with pride as her herd unwaveringly answered the challenge of the river. Soon they were clam-

bering, dripping and snorting, out on the other side. All had gone as smoothly as a greased sourdough biscuit.

For a moment, Star's foot slipped as she scrambled up the slippery bank, but in an instant she found firm footing, and they were safe on the other shore. They were across!

Emma Jane turned and waved to Easter, who was watching from the top of the bluff. As she did so, a big tree trunk, its tangled branches still outspread, floated gently by. Emma Jane felt a shudder run clear to her toes as she realized the confusion and panic the bobbing tree trunk could have caused had it appeared a few minutes earlier.

Giving herself a quick shake, she turned back to the herd and found herself looking directly into the glaring blue eyes of the man she had met by the river. His red beard bristled with indignation as he thundered, "*Where is your trail boss?* Of all the downright stupid things I ever saw, this beats 'em all—to let a mite of a gal like you swim across a swift rampagin' river—where is your trail boss?"

Muddy water was dripping from Emma Jane's clothes, but she pulled herself tall in the saddle and met his gaze straight on. "*I'm* the trail boss, Mister."

"*You're* the trail boss!" Emma Jane had heard that same note of disbelief before. "But your pa—you told me your whole family was goin' back to Illinois!"

"That's right." Emma Jane was meekly polite. "Ma's driving the covered wagon with the little ones. Martin, Easter, and I take care of the herding—and *that's* all the family we've got now, Mister."

He stared at her in open-mouthed amazement. "Well, I'll be danged! How far you come like this?"

"Waco. We left Waco in mid-April."

"Clear from Waco—well, I'll be danged—and plannin' on goin' clear to Chicago—well, I'll be——! But this is no job for a mite of a gal!" The roar rose again and the red beard flashed. "You can't do it!"

"Oh, yes, I can! I'm *doin'* it, Mister."

For a moment, the fiery red beard shook in anger. Then the quivering thatch of red quieted. A look of admiration swept away the indignation in the man's face.

"By the great horn spoon, I guess you are! You've got plenty of spunk. With a bit of luck you might make it at that. You might make it at that!"

"Thanks, Mister. Pa said he *knew* I could do it. And I reckon I will."

*Emma Jane did make it to Chicago. And there was hardly a cowhand in Illinois who didn't hear about the "trail boss in pigtails" who had brought a herd of longhorn steers all the way from Texas!*

# Whoopee Ti Yi Yo, Git Along, Little Dogies

As I walked out one morning for pleasure,
I spied a cowpuncher a-ridin' alone;
His hat was thrown back and his spurs was a-jinglin',
As he approached me a-singin' this song,

*Whoopee ti yi yo, git along, little dogies,*
*It's your misfortune, and none of my own.*
*Whoopee ti yi yo, git along, little dogies,*
*For you know Wyoming will be your new home.*

Early in the spring we round up the dogies,
Mark 'em and brand 'em and bob off their tails;
Round up our horses, load up the chuck-wagon,
Then throw the dogies upon the old trail.

It's whooping and yelling and driving the dogies;
Oh, how I wish you would go on!
It's whooping and punching and "Go on little dogies,
For you know Wyoming will be your new home."

. . .

*Whoopee ti yi yo, git along, little dogies,*
*It's your misfortune, and none of my own.*
*Whoopee ti yi yo, git along, little dogies,*
*For you know Wyoming will be your new home.*

John A. Lomax

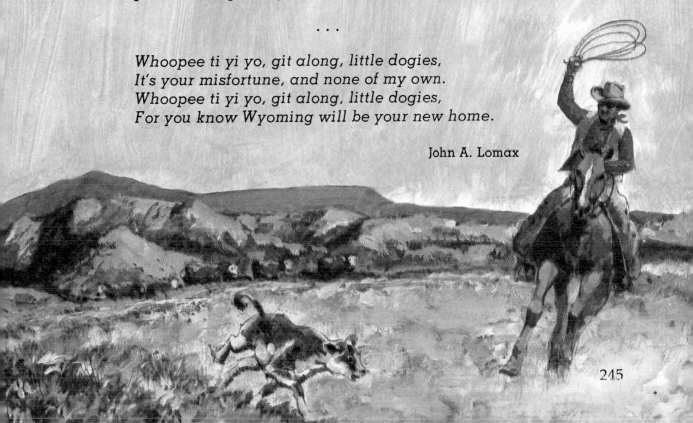

245

# "You Press the Button, We Do the Rest"

by Elizabeth Rider Montgomery

Almost anyone can take pictures nowadays. Even a small child can take very good snapshots with a simple camera. It is no trick at all to look in the viewfinder, snap the shutter, and do whatever is necessary before taking another picture.

On a trip, you can take all the pictures you wish with a small camera and some film. But a hundred years ago,

you would have found that taking pictures was a serious and complicated business. As an amateur photographer going out for a day's trip, you would have looked like an explorer heading for a long stay in the trackless wilderness! You would have had to carry not only a camera, which was quite big and heavy, but plenty of bulky glass plates for film, as well as your darkroom!

To take a picture, you would have set up the camera on a tripod and focused it on the object to be photographed. Then you would have set up the darkroom in a lightproof tent, where you would have spread collodion on a glass plate and dipped the whole thing in an acid bath. With the plate still dripping, you would have rushed to the camera, slid the plate in, and exposed the picture. Then you would have taken the plate to the darkroom to develop the picture before it spoiled. When you had finished developing the pictures, you would have had to pack up the equipment and carry it home.

So you can readily believe that you would have had to be quite enthusiastic about photography to take pictures in the 1800's.

George Eastman was one of those people who were really enthusiastic about photography. When he went on a trip, he liked to take back to his mother, who could not go with him, pictures of what he had seen. But he did not like the bulky glass plates, the complicated camera, the nuisance of carrying a darkroom around. He thought the business of taking pictures ought to be made easier. He began to dream of making photography so simple that anyone could take pictures. Soon George Eastman was spending all his spare time—he was a bank clerk—experimenting with photography.

When he read of a dry-plate process, developed in England, he was delighted. A dry plate would do away with the nuisance of handling a wet plate. No more need to carry collodion or acid around. No more necessity of having a darkroom on a trip. The plates could be developed when one reached home.

"But," thought Eastman, "it still isn't simple enough. Glass plates of any kind are hard for the amateur photographer to handle. They are heavy to carry, and they are likely to break. No, what's needed is something unbreakable, something light and flexible that might roll up inside the camera. That's what I want to find."

For years Eastman worked and experimented. He quit his bank job, started a small factory, and made dry plates. They were very popular because they were so much easier to use than the old wet plates. The factory did well, but Eastman began experimenting with other materials besides glass, trying to find a flexible film. At last he found that he could coat paper with a gelatin substance and make a film that was flexible enough to be rolled. He was now ready to make a camera that anyone could use.

When his first camera was finished in 1888, it was a little black box, nearly square. A tripod was no longer a necessity, for the camera could be held in one's hands. The paper film, coated with the gelatin substance and put on a roll, was inside the camera. The roll held enough film for one hundred exposures. All a photographer would have to do was to focus the desired object in the viewfinder, press the button, and turn the roll for the next exposure. After a hundred pictures were taken, the photographer would send the camera back to Eastman's factory, where the film would be developed and printed.

George Eastman was delighted with this little camera. He was certain it would accomplish what he had dreamed of—making photography so easy that anyone and everyone could take pictures.

When production of the new camera was underway in his factory, Eastman undertook to make up a name for it. With a pencil and a pad of paper in hand, he sat under a shaded lamp one night, thinking. In advertising, he intended to use the sentence, "You press the button, we do the rest." He believed the name for his product would be as important as all the advertising he could do. And he intended to coin a name so unusual and distinctive that it would easily be recognized and remembered—a name that would be associated with his new, simple, little camera.

How should he start? Should he take two already known words, such as *camera* and *easy*, and put parts of them together to make one word?

"No," Eastman decided. "This name shall not be made up of other words. I shall make a really *new* word."

He had always liked the letter "K." It seemed so firm, so interesting. So he put "K" down on the paper. Now what would go with "K"? At once the letter "O" leaped into his mind, so he wrote it beside the "K."

"KO," read Eastman. "That's a good first syllable. Short and crisp. Now for a second syllable."

Eastman thought for a long time. Then he set down another "K" at a little distance from his "KO." Beginning and ending the name with "K" seemed a good idea.

It was hours before the other letters fell into place. But when at last he wrote "D" and "A" in the blank space, Eastman knew he had exactly the name he was looking for: Kodak! "Ko" sounded much like the button as it was pressed; "dak," like the click of the shutter. And the whole name was easy to say and easy to remember. Yet it was distinctive—a name that could be associated with a distinctive camera. Kodak! Yes, that was a good name.

As almost everyone know, the Kodak served its purpose of making picture taking easy enough and cheap enough so that practically anyone could do it. And it soon made snapshots as common and as popular as George Eastman had hoped. Though another material was soon discovered for making the film, and the film was made much shorter, the word Kodak continued to stand for easy, quick picture taking. Though other improvements have been made, Kodak is still known the world over.

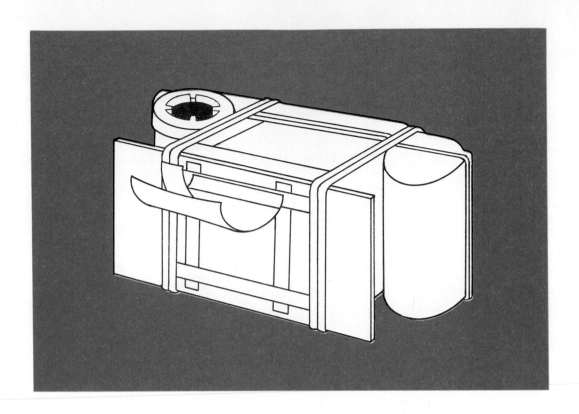

## How to Make and Use
## a Cartridge Pinhole Camera

By using only common household materials, you can make a camera that will produce pictures. A pinhole camera is a small, lighttight box with a black interior and a tiny hole in the center of one end. The pinhole itself has a cover that keeps light from entering the camera when you aren't taking a picture.

A cartridge pinhole camera is very easy to use because you can load and unload the camera in daylight. You can take at least twelve pictures without changing the cartridge. And you can have your photo dealer process the film.

## Materials

Here are the materials you will need to make a cartridge pinhole camera:

  1 cartridge of film, size 126, such as KODAK TRI-X Pan Film or KODAK VERICHROME Pan Film for black-and-white prints, or KODACOLOR II Film for color prints
  1 piece of thin black cardboard, 1¼ by 5¾ inches
  1 piece of heavy black cardboard, 1½ by 2¾ inches, with a ½-inch-square opening cut in the center
  1 piece of heavy aluminum foil, 1 inch square
  1 piece of black paper, 1 inch square
  1 wooden tongue depressor
  2 strong rubber bands
  1 No. 10 sewing needle
  black masking tape

## Assembling the Camera

1. Measure and mark the large piece of black cardboard into four sections, each 1 7/16 inches wide. If you do not have black cardboard, line any other piece of cardboard with black construction paper. The black lining will make sure the camera has a black interior.

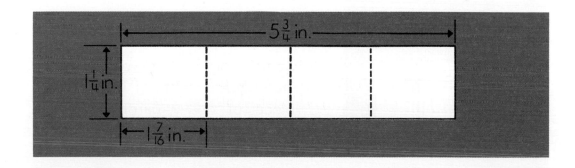

2. Using a knife, cut through only the top layer of card-board along each of the lines. This will make the cardboard easier to fold.

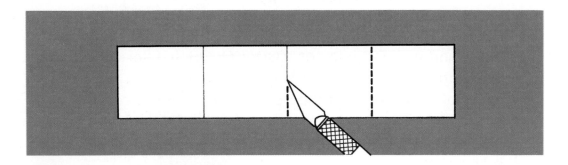

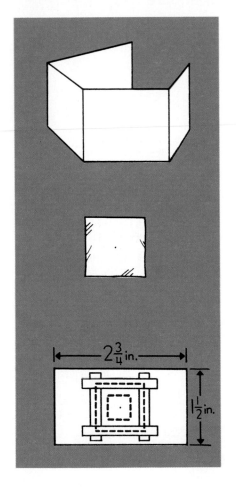

3. Fold the cardboard and tape the edges together with the black tape. This is your camera box.

4. Using *only the point* of the sewing needle, make a very tiny pinhole in the center of the aluminum foil. When you make the hole, rest the foil on a hard, flat surface.

5. Center the pinhole over the ½-inch-square opening in the small piece of heavy cardboard. Tape the foil to the cardboard on all four edges.

6. Put the 1-inch piece of black paper over the pinhole. Tape the top edge of the paper to the cardboard. Place a small piece of tape at the bottom of the black paper to hold it down between exposures.

7. Tape the cardboard with the pinhole to the box, using plenty of tape. Make sure that all the edges are taped together. In this way no light can get into the camera box.

8. Place the camera box into the grooved recess in the square opening of the film cartridge. This should be a tight fit so that no light can get into the camera.

9. Use the two strong rubber bands to hold the sections in place, and the camera is assembled.

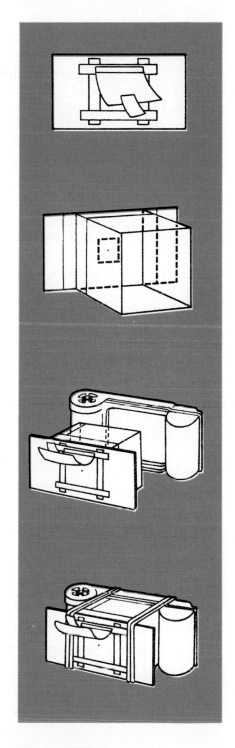

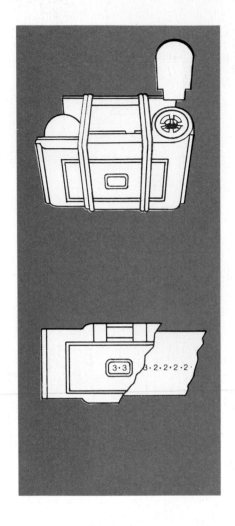

10. Trim the wooden tongue depressor to make a stick that will fit into the round opening in the cartridge. Place the camera so that the round chamber with the openings is on the right as you look at the label side of the cartridge. Place the stick in the round opening on the top of the chamber.

11. To advance the film, turn the stick *counterclockwise.* The yellow paper, seen through the small window on the label side of the film cartridge, should move. The film has numbers printed on it. Turn the stick slowly until the *third* and *fourth* numbers in each series show in the window. The film will then be in the proper position for picture taking.

## Taking a Picture

Your camera must be kept very still while you are taking a picture. Try taping the camera to a table, windowsill, chair, rock, or other flat surface. You can also use a lump of modeling clay to mount the camera firmly on a steady support. A kitchen stool will do nicely. Aim your camera by sighting over the top surface.

Be sure to use the small piece of tape to hold the black paper down over the pinhole after each exposure. This prevents light from entering your camera and spoiling the picture.

The following table, provided by Eastman Kodak Company, gives exposure recommendations for a cartridge pinhole camera. These recommendations are *approximate.* It is a good idea to make three different exposures for each setting. This way you will improve your chances of getting a good picture. So take one picture at the recommended exposure time. Take another picture at twice the recommended time. Then take a third picture at one half the time.

| KODAK Film | Bright Sun | Cloudy Bright |
|---|---|---|
| TRI-X Pan | ½ to 1 second | 2 to 4 seconds |
| VERICHROME Pan | 2 seconds | 8 seconds |
| KODACOLOR II | 3 seconds | 12 to 15 seconds |

*Pictures made with a cartridge pinhole camera.*

# Cameras and Courage

by Iris Noble

In the warm dusk of the New Jersey evening, Margaret's mother led her off the lighted porch and down onto the front lawn. They were to play a game, she explained. Margaret was to run around the house one way, her mother would run the other way, and they would meet and see who had run the faster.

"Run!" Mrs. White urged, picking up the long, ankle-length skirt and starting off to the left.

Margaret looked at her mother's back and then at the shadowy path to the right of the house. This was a dreadful game; she did not want to play. At six years of age, Margaret was so timid that almost everything scared her. Animals were terrifying. Bugs, and anything that crept or crawled or slithered, frightened her into screams. Her sleep was haunted by thoughts of burglars. She wept when she was left alone in the house by her family, even for ten minutes. But what she feared most was darkness and the night.

She took a hesitating step, back towards the safety of the lighted porch, but her mother called again—"Run!" And as much as she dreaded going off alone into the dark, she simply could not disobey or disappoint her beloved mother.

So she ran. Immediately around the corner of the house and away from the lighted porch, she was plunged into deep shadow, with the path only faintly visible ahead of her. Her heart began to pound. Terrors were all about, menacing her. Something waved over her head, dipped towards her, and brushed her forehead with damp fingers. Margaret's throat froze so tight that she couldn't scream. She could only whimper. She would have to turn back. She would have to turn back. She couldn't go on.

Then there was her mother's gentle laugh and her mother's arms tight around her. Margaret's throat unfroze, and she could laugh, too, as they walked back the same way she had come. The fearful thing with the damp fingers turned out to be a lilac branch, wet with dew. "Didn't you know?" asked Mrs. White. "Really?"

Yes, of course she had known. Even in the worst of her terror, she had smelled the familiar lilac smell and seen the fireflies dancing in the bush. She *had* known.

Even at six she had learned something important—that fear could make her believe what she knew was not so.

"Now, we'll play again," said her mother.

This time, up to and past the lilac bush, Margaret was not a bit afraid, although the terror came back when she found she had to go farther this time before her mother met her. Again they laughed, and Mrs. White guided Margaret's hands to touch the trailing vine that had seemed like a horrible snake. They walked back. Even in the dark, the path was becoming something familiar, something safe.

The next evening and the next and the next, the two played the game. By the end of the week, Margaret ran almost the whole way alone. Finally the evening came when she dared her mother, "You sit on the porch and wait. I'm going to run all around the house by myself!" And she touched the lilac bush as she went by, carelessly kicking aside the trailing vine, and ignoring the big watering can that had once set her heart thumping. She even stopped for a second to watch the fireflies sending signals to one another. Then she rounded the last corner and came to the porch in triumph.

That particular fear had been conquered, but there were still others. Luckily for timid Margaret, she had unusual parents. Years later, she would be as famous for her extraordinary courage and fearless adventures as she was for her photography. She would tell how her parents, Joe and Minnie White, helped her conquer fear. They never scolded her for it; they coaxed her out of it.

"Face your fears," insisted Mrs. White, "and then *do* something." The doing-something was the important part of the theory.

The entire White family were energetic doers. Margaret had been born on June 14, 1906, when children had neither radio nor television to amuse them. Games simply for amusement were scorned in her home. Margaret's brother Roger spent his evenings repairing or constructing mechanical things. Her sister Ruth read or sewed or helped their mother. Her father, a talented inventor, bent silently over his drawing board, endlessly absorbed in improving his inventions.

They were busy, energetic people. If they needed something in the cellar or the attic, they got it. If they needed a sharp tool, they used it. They could get so interested in a book they would not know what was going on in the house. It was strange to have someone like Margaret in the family.

Ruth, three years older, helped. She found out that Margaret frequently woke at night and lay sleepless and terrified, certain that burglars were moving about downstairs. "Wake me next time," said Ruth.

That very night she was roused when Margaret whispered, "They're here, downstairs. I can hear them!"

Ruth listened. True enough, there were small creakings and little noises from below. "Come on." Forcing herself wide awake, the older sister threw back the covers and got out of bed, pulling Margaret out, too. Hand in hand, they went down the stairs in the dark. This was not much easier for a nine-year-old girl than for one of six, but Ruth pretended she didn't mind. They went all over the lower half of the house, into every single room. There were no burglars.

There were only the safe, ordinary, everyday things— the chairs and tables, the stove in the kitchen, the dishes on the shelves, the food in the cupboards. The sounds, Ruth explained, were just the natural creaking of a house settling in the coolness of night, or the movement of a window shutter in the wind.

Margaret was completely satisfied. Never again did she wake in terror at night.

Her older sister helped in other ways, too. Margaret had an unusual head for heights. She could climb up on anything and balance on the knife-edge of nothing. So, when the two girls walked to school in the small town of Bound Brook, New Jersey, they scorned the sidewalks. It was a point of honor with them that they could make almost their whole way from home to school by using only the tops of fences, no matter how high they were. Margaret took the lead, with Ruth teetering behind, admitting that the height bothered her, and praising her small sister's ability.

The person who finally helped Margaret conquer all fear was her father. She loved him, as did the whole family. But he was so often absorbed with his mechanical inventions that he would spend whole evenings without saying a word to anyone, making notes even when he was at the dinner table. So it was a treat when, on rare occasions, he took Margaret alone or with the others on nature trips. Then he talked with them.

Both Joe and Minnie Bourke White were amateur naturalists. They wanted their children to love flowers and plants, birds and animals, bugs and reptiles, as much as they did. When the family picnicked in the meadows and woods around Bound Brook, it was an occasion to listen, watch, observe, and learn.

Margaret wanted to go on the picnics, but she was scared to tears by many things. The first time her father told her to hold out her hand while he put a small, furry caterpillar onto her palm, she shrieked and flung it off and cried for five minutes. Then her father came and sat down beside her and held out his own hand with a caterpillar on it.

Gently he talked with her while they both studied the tiny creature. He told Margaret how harmless it was, what it ate, and all about its life cycle. He let it crawl back on the leaf. Then both he and Margaret bent their heads close to the caterpillar to see its coloration.

After a while he brought her another. Although she trembled, she touched the caterpillar with her finger. "It's so soft!" she exclaimed. Something as soft as that didn't seem very dangerous. Before her father put it back on its leaf she let him transfer it to her fingers for just a second.

Again her father talked, of caterpillars, moths, and butterflies. He told about the marvels of spiders spinning their webs and the organization of ant life. Along with her desire to please him, Margaret's own curiosity was greatly stirred. The third time he brought her a caterpillar, the flesh of her hand shrank, but she accepted it and let it move on her palm. The next time she thought of nothing except how fascinating a creature it was.

By the end of that summer, she could pick up frogs. She could stand still and let a bird fly near her. She could laugh at the tickle of a daddy longlegs crawling on her bare arm.

The summer she was seven, she was beginning to hold and examine anything her father brought her. When she was eight, she had to be told that some snakes were dangerous, because she had become so entranced by them. Margaret had found that snakes were not clammy or unpleasant to touch. She was so proud of conquering her fears that she boasted: Let others have birds or kittens for pets, she wanted snakes. When she grew up, she was going to work with all kinds of reptiles.

This was a little more than the family had bargained for; but her parents believed in encouraging their children's interests. So Mr. White bought Margaret an old puff adder—harmless, but terrifying to look at. It was added to the collection of local snakes she had gathered herself. Her pets were supposed to live in cages, but usually they were found wandering about the house.

Visitors were known to turn green when they came upon Mrs. White reading in front of the fireplace, with Margaret's puff adder curled up in her lap.

Margaret told everyone that she would become a herpetologist, an expert on snakes. She would travel all

over the world, she said, and collect rare snakes. What if she married? Well, then she would marry a herpetologist, and they could study snakes together.

One summer she raised two hundred caterpillars that she had collected from the meadows and woods. She kept them under glass, fed them their favorite leaves, and watched and waited to see them become moths or butterflies. So interested was she in watching for the least movement, that one evening the family left her to watch while they went out.

Margaret was not aware of their going. Not until they returned did she realize that her last and most deep-seated fear had been conquered. She had stayed alone in the house and had been too interested to be afraid.

Her mother was right. "Face your fears and then *do* something," she had said. While Margaret was busy watching the caterpillars, her fears had vanished, never again to return.

So, by the time she was ready for college, she was an unusually fearless girl, with unusual interests. Not only did snakes fascinate her, but she had learned from her father and her brother that machinery could be very interesting, too. Once she had gone with her father to a foundry and had seen the glowing furnace of hot, molten steel. It had thrilled her in a way she could never explain to her friends.

Margaret was to discover a new interest when she enrolled in a college photography course. Mrs. White learned about the course and sent her youngest daughter a present—an Ica Reflex camera. The camera, considered quite fine for its day, was cheap at twenty dollars because it had a crack through its lens.

Margaret liked the camera and she liked the course. The teacher was exceptionally good. He had a way of making photography seem more important than just taking snapshots of family picnics.

He talked about the history of photography and the difficulties that had been overcome to make picture taking simple enough for everyone to enjoy. Margaret learned how George Eastman had brought out his Kodak camera in 1888. From that day, photography was in the hands of every person who wanted to press a shutter and snap a picture.

Margaret enjoyed the class, but her real interest was still herpetology.

# On Her Own

During her last year of college Margaret had to find work. She had saved a little money, but not enough to see her through. Every time she applied for a job, she was told, "Sorry, the job is taken."

She hadn't realized there were so many other students who needed work to get them through college. Thoroughly alarmed, she wondered: What was she to do? Without money she would not be able to stay. If she could not stay, she would never become a professional herpetologist.

One beautiful day she wandered about the Cornell campus, looking at the lovely library tower, the other fine buildings, and the green lawns. At last she came to a waterfall and sat down and looked at it. Suddenly tears welled up. She did not cry, but the tears blurred her eyesight so that the great falling waters were clouded and misty, shimmering with rainbows.

The sight was so beautiful! Margaret dried her eyes and remembered the Ica Reflex camera with the cracked lens that her mother had bought her three years earlier. At least she could take pictures of this waterfall and the campus buildings, so that even if she had to leave Cornell, she could carry the pictures with her always.

At that moment an idea came to her: Why not make and sell pictures? If she wanted to have the campus scenes on print to treasure always, others might also want them. Would they want the pictures badly enough to buy them?

It was a wild idea. Margaret had no assurance that she could take good pictures or that anyone would buy them if she did. Nevertheless, it was the only idea she had for making any money, and she determined to try it.

All that autumn, while Cornell and the surrounding countryside grew more beautiful with each changing month, Margaret took pictures. She wanted them to look like paintings, so she purposely made dreamy, soft-focus pictures. The waterfalls gleamed through misty sprays. The sharp outlines of the buildings were seen as if in twilight, shot through with the last glow of sunset.

She remembered what she had learned in her photography course, but actually she was still a beginner. It was not enough, she found, to point the camera at an object and hope to get a good picture. Sometimes it was just as important to leave out material as it was to get it in.

268

Suddenly she found herself thrilling to the camera. Classes were unbearable at times, when outside the classroom windows she could see a few white clouds in a blue sky. She wanted those clouds. Any building, she felt, looked far more interesting against clouds than it did against a clear sky.

Sometimes, she found, a person standing at the base of a building would help to show the real height of the building, while a tall building alone might seem quite ordinary. She began to realize that some of her pictures were out of balance, too fussy, or too crowded. Lights and shadows were tricky things. But when a picture pleased her, she studied it to find out why.

Maddening as many of her mistakes were, and costly as they were, she kept on. The camera slowly began to seem a part of her fingers and her eyes. But it was hard work, just the same.

She could not afford to have experts clean and service her camera, and so she learned to do it herself. She could not afford to have her film developed by others, so she arranged with a photographer to use his darkroom and develop her own prints.

Then came the printing on paper and the enlarging. All of this took time and learning and effort. Her darkroom technique did not yet equal her growing talent with the camera, although she was learning how to work with acids and different solutions. She made all the usual mistakes, such as opening the door into the darkroom and letting in light. She made that mistake only once. Never again.

Just before Christmas she displayed her best photographs and announced that she would take orders for any prints desired. To her astonishment, the orders came in so fast that she needed help to fill them.

After Christmas she went on to make more and more pictures. It was becoming an excitement she could not forgo. When ice formed on the waterfalls and snow covered the campus, blanketing trees and roofs of buildings, she felt an urge to photograph everything she saw.

No longer did she try for the soft-focus, blurry film that imitated paintings. The white snow; the clean, dark edges of buildings; and the black shadows were too beautiful to be disguised.

She was becoming fascinated by everything the camera could do. She was also finding beauty in objects not ordinarily considered beautiful. Anyone could appreciate a waterfall, but Margaret could make a striking picture of an icicle hanging from the roof above a window.

As more and more people saw Margaret's pictures, they told her that she was an exceptionally talented photographer. Was she going to take this up as a career?

Such a thought had never occurred to her. A professional photographer? She hadn't planned to be any kind of a photographer. It was now close to graduation, and she had been offered a job by the Curator of Herpetology at the Museum of Natural History in New York. For this she had studied and trained. Could she give this up for a career with a camera? Did she want to?

The answer was yes. Margaret had found that photography was more important to her than her old interests.

After graduation she decided to open a small studio in Cleveland. One of her reasons for choosing Cleveland was the area known as the Flats. The Flats had the buildings she wanted to photograph.

That section of Cleveland known as the Flats would not appeal to many persons' taste. Cleveland citizens did not take visitors there to show it off, as they proudly did other sections. In fact, unless Clevelanders had to work there, they tended to avoid going to the Flats, looking at the Flats, or even thinking about them. Factories were necessary, but not pretty.

It was an area of steel mills and foundries and factories and railroad yards, forbidding steel fences and over-

head cranes and dirty buildings—and Margaret loved it. She had a sense of wonder and excitement about industry.

She wandered about, camera in hand, all through the streets and saw a beauty in the Flats that no one else saw. Even before she got her first job, she was taking pictures—of railroad tracks where the singing rails seemed to spin off into space; of trucks being loaded, where men worked with rhythm; of dirty buildings that made mysterious shapes against an evening sky. And—oh!—how she wanted to get inside for other pictures!

That was forbidden, especially in the steel mills, where she most wanted to go.

In the meantime, though, Margaret enjoyed walking up and down the streets and looking for unusual and likely shots. One such opportunity came on a day when she did not have a camera. As she walked by a Cleveland square, she saw a man standing on a soapbox, preaching. He was utterly absorbed in his message, his arms uplifted, and totally unaware that the only congregation listening to him was a flock of pigeons at his feet. It was a marvelous picture.

Quickly Margaret looked about her and saw a camera shop. She dashed over. Could she rent or borrow a camera? Breathlessly she managed to explain and was astonished when the man behind the counter handed her a camera without any assurance that she would bring it back. She raced back to the square and got the picture. The pigeons were fluttering around the feet and knees of the preacher and looking as if they really cared what he said.

When she returned the camera, she introduced herself to the clerk, Alfred Hall Bemis. Although he was much older than Margaret, he shared her interest in picture taking and became her lifelong friend. They were soon ''Maggie'' and ''Beme'' to each other, arguing and discussing the problems faced by photographers.

# Fearless Adventure

The biggest problem Margaret faced was how to get inside a steel mill. She could remember the very moment when, as a child, she had gone to the foundry with her father and had watched the pouring of the hot, molten steel. She wanted to catch that magnificent moment on film.

The answer to that problem finally came when she was introduced to Elroy Kulas, the president of the Otis Steel Company. Elroy Kulas was a big industrialist, a powerful and awe-inspiring man. Yet Margaret found that she could talk with him as she had never spoken with anyone else of her feeling for industry and its enormous importance. She told him of her desire to capture its strength, its beauty and ugliness on film. Especially she wanted to photograph the pouring of steel ingots.

Mr. Kulas understood. He felt the same way she did, but he was curious. Did she expect to sell the pictures to him? Margaret shook her head. She wasn't selling prints. This was not why she asked permission. Let her see what she could do first. She wanted to photograph the steel mill for her own reasons. Afterwards, if he liked what she had done, they could talk about selling and buying.

Mr. Kulas gave orders throughout the entire mill that Margaret Bourke-White was to have the run of the place, so long as she did not interfere with the work or endanger herself or others. He himself would not be on hand because he was just leaving for six months in Europe.

Those six months were the best break Margaret had. Mr. Kulas had not realized that she meant to be in his mill night after night, week after week. Yet his orders giving her a free hand stood while he was gone.

At last she was inside! On the first few nights she wandered around, letting the workers and foremen and superintendents get used to her and her cameras. Soon they accepted her without any special notice when she stood beside them to get her pictures. Those early nights were a foretaste of what she could expect—the heat in some parts of the mill, the cold in other parts, the acid fumes, and the lighting problems. The huge building was designed for steel and not for photography.

It was not every night that they poured, and Margaret waited anxiously for the first one. Alfred Bemis went with her, and they stood watching on a high catwalk. When the fiery, liquid metal poured out of the furnace into ladles, Margaret went almost wild with excitement, snapping picture after picture. She moved about on the high walk in her high-heeled shoes with an utter disregard for her safety. With the pour just below, Beme had to hang on to her to keep her steady.

The excitement was so great that her letdown the next day was all the worse. She cried. In all those films she had taken, nothing came out of the flaming molten steel except a small circle of light among a jumble of shadows.

Finally, she wiped her eyes and went back to Otis Steel, more determined than ever. Somehow she would learn how to photograph under the poor lighting conditions. The white heat of the metal, she realized, was far more heat than light.

This was 1927, and what today is considered ordinary photographic equipment—flashbulbs, high-speed flash equipment, and flood lamps—had not yet been invented or were not in common use. Margaret knew nothing of them. She had to work with the light she had. She knew, also, that she needed a faster lens. She bought what she could, and Beme borrowed others from the store.

Finally, the six months were almost up. Mr. Kulas would be returning. If all she had to show him of a pour was the disappointing shots, it was most unlikely that he would extend his permission. He would probably be shocked to find how often she had entered his mill while he was away. There was to be one more pouring, and she went to Beme in desperation about it.

He telephoned her in excitement the next day. A salesman of photographic equipment, a friend of his, had come into the store with a new kind of huge flare. What he had were only samples, and he had none to spare, since he was on his way to sell them to the motion-picture studios. But Beme had convinced him to accompany Margaret and himself to the steel mill and to use at least one of his precious flares for the pouring.

The night came, and Margaret went to Otis Steel with Beme and Jack Jackson, the salesman. It was a miserable winter night, cold and snowy. As they waited for the pouring, the three of them shook from the icy drafts that blew through the building. Margaret's fingers grew numb, and she rubbed each one into life and feeling. They must not fail her tonight. Her feet were freezing, but she was too excited to care about them.

She had stationed herself and her two helpers on the catwalk above the pouring, and she held her reflex camera steady on a wooden railing, pointing downwards.

Then the hot metal began to flow. Jack and Beme each held onto a flare by its wooden handle. There was still not enough light. The salesman, entering into the excitement of the moment, gave himself and Beme each another flare. They held the flaming light in both hands while Margaret steadily took pictures. The flares lasted half a moment, then died away, much to Margaret's intense regret because the pouring was still going on below.

Then she saw that Jack had lit more flares. He was giving her every single one of his samples. Joyfully she shot on and on, while Jack and Beme held up the flares. The tremendous heat from the ingot molds below burned their faces. The molds filled slowly. Margaret took pictures of every ladle as it emptied its burning flow. Finally the very last ladle dripped splashes of white-hot steel into the ingot molds, like a fountain spray arching downwards.

The prints she and Beme developed the next night turned out to be wonderful. Everything was there—the ladles and the men behind them in their heatproof clothes and face protectors, the cranes and the furnace, the molten steel, the blazing liquid forming in the molds. But there was one picture that puzzled them for a second. It seemed to be scratched with arched lines. Then they realized, yelling with excitement, that those arched lines were the actual flow of drops and sparks in the final shot of the very last pouring.

Margaret had captured liquid steel in motion!

The small prints were beautiful, but when enlarged they were awful. The flare of light became dull. The enlarging paper was at fault. Then, once again, a salesman friend of Beme's came to the rescue. He had a new paper, and Margaret found that on that paper the enlargements came out very well.

So well, in fact, that upon his return, Mr. Kulas studied them with delighted amazement. "Magnificent," he said. He had no idea anyone could get such pictures. Probably, at that time, no one else had.

How much, he asked, did Margaret want for the pictures? She took her courage in hand and explained to him that the pictures were worth either nothing or a lot. If they really meant something to him, she would have to ask one hundred dollars for a single picture.

Mr. Kulas didn't even look startled. He was still studying the photographs and thinking about them. He just nodded and said, absentmindedly, that he didn't think the price was too much, not at all.

Then he leaned back in his chair and told her what he wanted: eight of these pictures and quite a few more. He

also wanted her to take other shots which he would choose, in both the action and the setting. He wanted to put all the photographs together to make a book which he would call *The Story of Steel.*

Margaret felt she had never known a happier moment. Her pictures were to be used for just what she would have wanted: to tell the story of the steel industry.

Mr. Kulas wanted to know if she was ever afraid when she was balancing on narrow ledges or creeping along the floor, getting closer and closer to the intense heat and acid fumes of the pouring. And if she wasn't afraid, why wasn't she?

Margaret explained that she had been born with a good head for heights, and she told about her fence-walking to school. "The trick," she said, "is to pretend you are only a foot off the ground. Then you aren't afraid and your feet are steady." But, yes, there had been times when she had known fear. Those times had been short-lived, however. She had forgotten to be afraid, being so absorbed in her work.

He liked that. Mr. Kulas was a man of importance and he gave her letters of introduction to other industrial presidents. When one of her steel-pouring pictures won a Cleveland Art Museum award, he was proud of her.

She got so much well-paid work during 1928 that she could afford all sorts of things—new cameras, new lenses, and new equipment. She bought a car and a few new clothes. But most thrilling of all, the day came when she could move her equipment out of her kitchen and bathroom and into a real studio.

"You're doing well, Maggie," said Beme. "And you deserve to."

Margaret's steel-pouring pictures were not only the realization of a dream, but they opened new doors of opportunity for her. She eventually became a well-known magazine photographer—known not only for her photography but also for her extraordinary courage and fearless adventures.

# His Inventions Saved Lives

by Robert C. Hayden

On July 25, 1916, a violent explosion ripped through Tunnel No. 5 of the Cleveland Waterworks. The tunnel was 250 feet below the surface of Lake Erie, and at the moment of the explosion more than 30 men were working there. Deadly gases, heavy smoke, and dust quickly filled the underground space, trapping the men inside.

Firefighters, doctors, nurses, police officers, and waterworks employees gathered at the tunnel's entrance. Relatives and friends of the trapped men stood hopefully by. No one knew the fate of the trapped workers. Their staying alive for more than a few hours wasn't likely. Someone would have to enter the tunnel if the men were to be found and carried out. But the heavy smoke and deadly gases made it impossible for anyone to try. Chances of saving the workers' lives seemed hopeless.

In the city of Cleveland, Garrett A. Morgan was resting at his home. Someone at the scene of the explosion remembered that a man had been demonstrating a gas inhalator. The man hoped to interest manufacturers in his invention. Garrett A. Morgan had received a patent for this invention. Later he had been awarded First Grand Prize at an international safety exhibition in New York City. But, because of race discrimination, he had not been too successful in selling the inhalator.

Now Morgan was contacted and asked to come to the Lake Erie tunnel as soon as possible. He was asked to bring several of his gas inhalators with him. Morgan arrived shortly, along with his brother. Quickly they and two other volunteers put on Morgan's gas masks. Then Morgan's team entered the tunnel in search of the trapped men. The gas masks allowed them to breathe clean air that was carried in the pouch of each inhalator. Garrett Morgan led the team in and out of the smoke-filled tunnel many times. Together, they saved the lives of thirty-two employees, carrying them out of the tunnel to the waiting crowd.

This heroic act drew a great deal of public attention. Suddenly manufacturers and fire departments all across the country became interested in Morgan's gas inhalator, or gas mask, as we would call it today. Orders for it poured into Cleveland from fire companies all over the United States. And Morgan was asked to talk about and demonstrate his invention in many cities and towns. For his courage he was awarded a medal by the City of Cleveland. But more important, his heroic act helped to prove the value of his invention.

In 1912, four years before the violent explosion in the Erie tunnel, Garrett A. Morgan had received a patent on his safety helmet. The helmet was designed for speedy work. It could be put on in seven seconds and taken

off in three, thus avoiding a costly delay. Clean air was supplied from a bag of air held in the rear by two tubes leading from the hood. There was enough air in the bag to allow a person to stay in a smoke- or gas-filled room from fifteen to twenty minutes.

Garrett A. Morgan was a man who was always trying out new ideas. On November 30, 1923, his experimenting again paid off when he was awarded a patent for inventing a three-way traffic signal.

The Go-Stop signals already in use were not very helpful because there was no neutral position. In other words, the signal indicated either stop or go. There was no yellow light as we know it today. Without a traffic officer present, the signals could be ignored. Morgan's three-way traffic signal was designed so that traffic could move in all directions, even when an officer was not present.

Morgan's invention also solved another problem. A traffic officer often failed to change the signal. This happened when an officer was tired or forgetful. The delays confused both the drivers and the pedestrians.

Figure 1

Figure 2

When Morgan's signal was at the half-mast, or neutral, position, as is shown in Figure 1, the drivers, using caution, could move in all directions—north, south, east, and west. This could take place even when a traffic officer was not present. The half-mast position was used at night to mark dangerous intersections. A driver approaching Morgan's signal in the half-mast position would do the same as today's driver would do when approaching a yellow light—slow down and proceed with caution.

When the signal was positioned as shown in Figure 2, the drivers could move in an east or a west direction. Those heading north or south would be held at a stand-still. To stop the east and west traffic, the signal post would be turned so that *Go* faced north and south, as shown in Figure 3. When the signal was positioned as

Figure 3    Figure 4

shown in Figure 4, traffic was stopped in all directions. This allowed pedestrians to proceed across the street in safety.

Morgan's traffic signal became the forerunner of the overhead and sidewalk lights that are seen today. Without such signals, there could be no orderly flow of traffic on our streets and highways. There could be no safe way for pedestrians to cross our busy intersections.

It would be difficult to know the number of lives that have been saved because of Garrett A. Morgan's inventions. Many soldiers of World War I owed their lives to the gas masks they wore on the battlefield. The traffic light system used in this country has protected thousands of lives on our streets, highways, and railways.

Morgan received several medals and citations during his lifetime. The National Safety Device Co. awarded him a First Grand Prize for his gas inhalator. The United States government gave him a citation for his traffic signal device. The International Association of Fire Chiefs awarded him a gold medal.

Garrett A. Morgan became almost blind during the last few years of his life. After he died in 1963, he was given national recognition at the Emancipation Centennial Celebration held in Chicago. Five months later, his granddaughter, Karen Morgan, wrote about her grandfather, recalling his life in this way:

> ". . . coming from a poor family, G. A. Morgan did all he could to enrich both his life and that of his family. He was a jolly man, although he had his stern moments, and was very quick-tempered and outspoken . . . he gained some foes, but he had many friends. . . .
>
> "Mr. Morgan was a down-to-earth practical man. He worked hard for everything he ever did or accomplished . . . He was a lover of the great outdoors . . . After he lost 90% of his sight he made constant use of his mind and his hands. He always kept himself busy. . . .
>
> "With all of his achievements, recognition, and possessions, one fact remained to be true until his last breath . . . he was a plain man . . . proud to be an American, proud of his race.
>
> "His last goal . . . in life was to be able to attend the Emancipation Centennial which was to be held in Chicago, in August of 1963. His wish was not fulfilled however, as he died one month before it was to take place. . . ."

# Through the Finish Line

# FELIX the FOURTH

by Mac Davis

Felix Carvajal was a humble and little-known mail carrier living in Havana, Cuba, at about the turn of the century. When the Olympic Games were staged at the World's Fair in St. Louis, Missouri, Felix became possessed with the crazy idea that he was a great runner. Fate, he believed, had destined him to go to the Olympic Games. There he would win the 26-mile marathon race for the glory of Cuba!

Of course, in his wild dream, Felix gave no consideration to the cold fact that he was not an athlete. He had never been in a competitive race, and never in his whole life had he run a long-distance race. Even so, he was convinced that he was destined to win the marathon. Felix Carvajal publicly announced his prospective trip to the Olympic Games and his expected triumph there.

Unfortunately, he had no money with which to finance the trip. To attract attention to his running skill, he ran around the public square in Havana until a crowd gathered. Then he begged for help. By repeated performances, Felix collected enough money to finance his trip to St. Louis.

The year was 1904, and Felix sailed by way of New Orleans. During his brief stop there he was waylaid by gamblers who cheated him of all his money. Broke and friendless in a strange city, Felix Carvajal was still determined to run in the Olympic marathon race. So he decided to run all the way from New Orleans to St. Louis—a distance of seven hundred miles!

He ran and he ran, eating whatever food he could beg from people along the way. He continued to run in a grim race against time. He finally arrived in St Louis, just in time for the start of the Olympic marathon race.

He came up to the starting line, worn, weary, and half-starved. He was wearing heavy walking shoes, a long-sleeved shirt, and long trousers. A friendly athlete took pity on him. With a pair of shears the athlete snipped off the sleeves and cut the trousers in half to make Felix look more like a runner in a track suit.

It was broiling hot as thirty-one long-distance runners from all over the world set off on that Olympic marathon. But only fourteen were able to finish the punishing grind of twenty-six miles and 385 yards. One of them was the mail carrier from Cuba, Felix Carvajal, who never before had run a competitive race. Surprisingly enough, he finished in fourth place. It was an astonishing performance!

Felix Carvajal is not listed in the Olympic record books as a marathon champion. But in sports memory, he is recalled as the incredible "Felix the Fourth." Felix the Fourth—the runner who, at the turn of the century, ran seven hundred miles to lose an Olympic marathon race.

## To James

Do you remember
How you won
That last race?
How you flung your body
At the start . . .
How your spikes
Ripped the cinders
In the stretch . . .
How you catapulted
Through the tape . . .
Do you remember?
Don't you think
I lurched with you
Out of those starting holes?

Don't you think
My sinews tightened
At those first
Few strides . . .
And when you flew into the stretch
Was not all my thrill
Of a thousand races
In your blood?
At your final drive
Through the finish line
Did not my shout
Tell of the
Triumphant ecstasy
Of victory?

Frank Horne

# The Girl
# Who Wouldn't Give Up

by Alex Haley

Wilma Rudolph was the seventeenth child in a Negro family in Clarksville, Tennessee. She weighed only four and a half pounds when she was born. And she was four years old before she could even toddle. Then this poor child came down with scarlet fever and double pneumonia. She lay near death for weeks. Finally she pulled through, but her left leg was paralyzed. Although the scarlet fever and pneumonia were gone, she was so badly crippled that she could not walk.

The Rudolph family had very little money, but Wilma's mother believed that her little girl had a right to be healthy. She wrapped her in a blanket and took her forty-five miles by bus to a medical clinic in Nashville. There, doctors gave Wilma many tests. They said she might be able to use her leg again—but only if it were massaged every day for years.

Mrs. Rudolph had a job as a maid, but she had one free day every week. For the next two years she used this day to make the long trip to Nashville with Wilma. The other six days she came home, tired from work, and fixed supper for her large family. Then she massaged the thin little leg until long after Wilma had fallen asleep. At the end of the first year, the doctors found the leg only a little better. So Mrs. Rudolph taught three older children how to massage it, too. After that Wilma's leg was rubbed four times a day. "She's going to walk," said Mrs. Rudolph.

### Making Up for Lost Play

By the time she was six years old Wilma could hop for short distances. Then her leg would buckle. At eight, she was able to walk with a leg brace. Later that year the doctors gave her a high-top shoe instead of the brace. And Wilma limped happily off to school.

One of Wilma's brothers, Westley, got a basketball. He put a peach basket up on a pole in the backyard. To the family's surprise, Wilma was soon playing basketball. In spite of her heavy shoe, she would dribble and cut, stop and go, keeping the ball away from Westley. Then she would spring into the air as she made a shot. When others stopped to rest, she would go on playing alone.

"She's making up for all the playing she's missed," said her mother.

One day Mrs. Rudolph came home to find Wilma bounding around under the peach basket, barefoot! She no longer needed the special shoe.

When Wilma entered high school, she went out for basketball. Once she was playing so hard she bumped right into the referee, Coach Clinton G. Gray.

"You're buzzing around like a skeeter wherever I turn," he said. From then on her nickname was "Skeeter."

Not long afterward, Coach Gray started a girls' track team. He saw Skeeter run, and timed her. Then he stared at his stopwatch in amazement. When the girls' high-school meet was held, she won the 50-, 75-, and 100-yard dashes.

Edward Stanley Temple, coach of women's track at Tennessee State University, was watching. With his crack team of "Tigerbelles" he was trying to win fame for this Negro university. And he saw a future champion in the young girl with the perfect sprinter's body, the long powerful legs, and the drive to win.

## Never Give Up

Each summer Mr. Temple tried out ten high-school girl track stars. Those who did well enough were given scholarships to the university. "Be glad to try you out," he told Wilma.

The news thrilled the Rudolph family. They had all helped Skeeter grow strong enough to run. "You're the first one in this house that ever had a chance to go to college," her mother told her. "If running's going to do that, I want you to set your mind to be the best. Never give up!"

With nine other speed stars from Negro high schools, Wilma arrived at Tennessee State that summer. Mr. Temple's first order was for a cross-country jog, some five miles across rough pastures. Halfway, many of the girls were sick and worn out. Wilma, too, stumbled and fell. But somehow they all dragged themselves back.

Mr. Temple greeted them bluntly: "If you want to run here, you have to be in good condition."

Next morning the girls were up at five. Each of them was paired with a Tigerbelle to do fifty-yard sprints. Every high-school runner finished yards behind, and Wilma did worse than most. When she got back to her room, she cried. She felt ashamed that she had come. But she thought of her mother's saying, "Never give up."

Edward Stanley Temple knew just how to make the girls want to win. He kept telling Wilma what was wrong with her style. "Stretch out those long legs—stride!" he told her. "Your elbows look like a windmill. Pump the arms straight. No tight fists—you run more relaxed with open palms."

He also knew when Wilma had had enough. "Look, Skeeter," he said, with kindness in his voice, "right now you are a fair runner. But I want great runners. My Tigerbelles make you look bad because they're better trained than you. Now you can go home if you want to. Or you can stay, and I'll teach you how to win races." He paused, and then he added, "I think you can be a champion if you want to."

## But Something Was Wrong

Three days later Wilma was included among the four Junior Tigerbelles Mr. Temple was taking with his college stars to Ponca City, Oklahoma. They were to participate in the National AAU (Amateur Athletic Union) meets. These four girls won the Junior Division's 400-yard relay. The college Tigerbelles swept all the Senior Division sprints and the relay. Tennessee State had its first AAU championship.

Wilma returned to her family and schoolmates a heroine — to everyone but herself. She still felt she could never run as well as Coach Temple's college girls. Her mother put her finger on the trouble. "It *looks* like you can't," she said. "But you mustn't *think* you can't. You just got to forget everything but trying."

Through the rest of her high-school summers, Wilma drilled in all the details of Tigerbelle style. By the time she entered the university, Mr. Temple was telling the other girls, "Watch Wilma!"

Over and over she would race a hundred yards. Then she would walk back to the starting line and race again. She had heard so many starting pistols and counted her early strides so often that, by now, instinct set her in motion. It told her the exact instant to begin straightening up and "floating" — and, seconds later, when to start leaning to meet the tape.

Everywhere they raced, the Tigerbelles were winners. With the three other members of the relay team Wilma ranked as one of the four fastest Tigerbelles. Yet, when they raced among themselves, the others always beat her.

"What's wrong?" Mr. Temple often asked.

"I don't know, Coach," she said. For she was trying with all she had.

Then, in November 1959, Wilma began suffering from a sore throat. Mr. Temple took her to a doctor, who took out her tonsils. "Those tonsils had been sapping her strength for years," the doctor said.

298

## A Great Race

Three weeks later, Wilma returned to the track. She was in full health for the first time in her life. At the Chicago Indoor AAU Nationals she blazed to first place in three races. At a later meet, she trimmed three tenths of a second off the Olympic and world 200-meter record. Tryouts for the 1960 Olympic Games were held at Abilene, Texas. There Wilma took the 100 and 200 meters. She anchored the winning Tigerbelle relay team.

"Somebody will have to set a new world record to beat her!" Mr. Temple exclaimed.

Seven Tigerbelles were among the three hundred and ten United States athletes who flew to Rome to take part in the Olympic Games in August 1960. There, in the 100-meter sprint, Wilma set a new Olympic record of eleven seconds flat. In the 200-meter finals, she won a breath-taking victory over Germany's star Jutta Heine.

Now it was time for the women's 400-meter relay! The people packing the huge stadium fell silent. Six teams were taking their places on the track. But all eyes were on one girl—Wilma Rudolph. If the United States team won this final, she would be the first American woman ever to win three gold medals in track.

A starting pistol cracked. The first runners shot from their starting blocks and raced the batons to the second. The second runners raced to the third. And now the third girl on the U.S. team was in the lead. She flashed toward Wilma, who had already started her forward motion.

Then a gasp went up from the crowd. The baton was fumbled, and Wilma had to stop to grasp it. Germany's Jutta Heine was flying two strides ahead. But now Wilma's long strides began to burn up the track. She came abreast of Jutta Heine . . . pulled slightly ahead . . . and burst the tape in first place. Wilma had managed to make up for the fumble by an incredible act of courage and determination.

## Queen of Track

The Tigerbelles had won the relay, and the lean brown girl from Tennessee was a three-time gold-medal winner! The noise in the stadium was deafening. "Wilma!" the crowd roared. "Skeeter!" Hats, newspapers, and programs rained down on the field as she half circled and jogged toward the sidelines.

"Coach Temple! Coach Temple!" Wilma was crying as athletes and photographers crowded around her. She was the world's Queen of Track. And she was weeping tears of thanks for her coach's patient training and for her mother's determination that a crippled child would walk.

When Wilma came home, every school and business in Clarksville was closed for "Welcome Wilma Day." The whole town lined the streets to cheer her. American sportswriters voted her "Woman Athlete of the Year." A year later she was given the James E. Sullivan award for being America's outstanding athlete, male or female. In 1962 she went on to break more world records as a sprinter, both at home and in Europe, to prove that she was still the fastest woman in the world.

But the girl from Clarksville is always humble and good-natured. Life means more to her than medals and meets. Her desire as a teacher and coach is to pass on to other children the important lesson she has learned—that those who really want to can win.

# The Mystery
# of Pelham House

by Joseph Raskin and Edith Raskin

In Pelham, Massachusetts, near the road that led to Pelham Bridge, there stood a quaint old house. Its doors were bolted, for no living person wanted to stay in it. According to an old tale, a young woman, Anne Hutchinson, and her family had once lived in a cabin nearby.

Anne and her family were killed one night, so the story goes, and their cabin burned to the ground. For a time Anne's spirit hovered over the smoldering ashes. Then her spirit, seeking shelter, moved into the bolted house to mourn her lot and to terrify the neighborhood with all kinds of pranks.

The young man who owned Pelham House lived most of the time in the big city. Being an adventurous young man and not believing in spirits, he decided to reopen the house. But hard as he tried, he could not find a caretaker in the neighborhood. Even those he brought from far away would not remain more than a day or two. Frightened by what they saw and heard during their brief stay, they spread strange tales about the house.

Equally strange were the tales of the teamsters who happened to pass the house late at night on their way to town. Some saw a light moving from room to room and heard a woman crying. Others claimed they saw the house all lit up. Still others saw the house violently shaking, as though invisible hands were trying to pull it off the ground.

It was no wonder that the townspeople were troubled when they heard of the young owner's intention to come and live in the house. They urged him to change his mind—to stay away from it and, if anything, add another lock. To their dismay the young owner merely laughed. "I'll risk it," he said.

It was early in the spring when he offered a farmer and his wife from a distant village the opportunity to come and take care of the house. The couple had only a vague idea what the house was like, and being badly in need of work, they readily accepted the offer. They were pleasantly surprised to find the inside of the house fitted up in good old Dutch-style furnishings. They were especially pleased with the fireplace, which was decorated with fine old Dutch tiles.

"Quite different from the tumble-down home we had!" the woman observed with a contented sigh.

Wasting no time, she went ahead cleaning up the house while her husband attended to the overgrown garden. There were heavy layers of rotting leaves that had collected over many years to cart away and dried-up brush to get rid of. The sun had made its full round in the sky when they finally decided that they had done enough work for the day.

The couple went to bed early. Although they heard some rumbling in the house, they were too tired to pay any attention to it.

The following morning the farmer went out again to work in the garden. He noticed that the teamsters whipped up their horses when passing the house. That was odd, he thought. Were they trying to let him know that he, being a stranger, was not welcome here?

It was noontime when his wife came running out of the house, looking alarmed. "The doors of all the rooms keep opening and closing all on their own!" she called.

"That doesn't make sense," her husband grumbled. Nevertheless, he followed her into the house. He went through all the rooms, but found everything quiet. "Must have been a sudden wind that caused it." He shrugged and went back to work.

During their evening meal no mention was made of her alarm. When darkness set in, they went to bed and fell asleep immediately.

In the middle of the night the farmer's wife sat up with a start and shook her husband awake. "Did you hear that noise?"

"What noise? What did you hear?" he asked.

"Babies crying something awful."

"You must have been dreaming," the farmer complained and pulled the blanket over his head.

He had hardly fallen asleep when he was wakened again. "There they go, crying again," whispered his wife.

The farmer listened, puzzled at the sound. "There must be an owl's nest in one of the trees. I'll find it tomorrow. Now try to sleep."

But the anxious woman did not close her eyes that night. She was certain it was not owls but babies crying.

The farmer did not bother to look for the owl's nest. A person was bound to hear strange noises in a country he was not familiar with, he reasoned. Just the same, when night came and he was ready to go to bed, he put a lighted lantern at his bedside. He tried to stay awake, but he was tired from the day's work and soon fell asleep.

It was close to midnight when a deafening bang woke him up. He saw his wife sitting up, terrified.

"Don't say I'm dreaming this time," she said.

The farmer had to agree that she was not dreaming. Doors kept creaking and banging as they opened and closed. It seemed as if there was a wild party going on and the guests were rushing from room to room having a merry time. Topping this noise came a crash as though all the dishes in the house were thrown to the ground.

The farmer remembered that the owner of the house had stored some dishes in one of the rooms. Bracing himself, he picked up the lantern and went to see what was going on there. He found the room in good order. The dishes that had been piled up on a table were still there, and not a single one was broken.

For a while he stood rubbing the back of his neck. "Now, what on earth could have caused that awful crash?" he kept asking himself. "And those doors banging!" He stepped out into the garden, expecting to meet with stormy weather. But the sky was dotted with stars, and there was not a breeze. "Well," he said, trying to reassure himself, "There's really nothing strange about the doors. All they need is fixing so that they close properly."

The next evening the husband sat before the warm fire to think about the house. What did he know about it? Perhaps he should make a thorough search.

While he was thinking this, the wall in front of him slowly opened, and a vapory shadow moved into the room. As it moved on, it gradually formed into a human figure. And when it reached the middle of the room, he could clearly see the features of a woman. She was young and graceful, and her long dark hair was streaming down over her shoulders. Her face was beautiful, but full of sorrow. She stood for a moment, silently regarding him. Then, gliding gracefully across the room, she disappeared through the wall—again a vapory shadow.

Thoroughly shaken up though he was by what he had seen, the farmer decided not to say a word about it. That night the couple was not troubled by any noise. But as soon as the sun rose the farmer woke his wife.

"Pack up our things. I have had enough of this house," he said. So they locked up and left.

The quaint old house was never reopened. No more did the teamsters, speeding past, notice any flickering lights coming from the house. No more did the towns-people hear talk of the owner's coming to live in it. But some occasionally claimed they had seen a woman leaning on her elbows and mournfully looking out of a window of Pelham House.

# Twelve Ounces of Courage

by Arthur Catherall

Flight Lieutenant Mikhandi Lal shot a quick glance at the instrument panel of his MIG fighter plane. He had flown twelve minutes northwest, close to 110 miles from his base. It was almost time to make the long right turn that would put him on the course he was to fly before coming in for a mock attack.

There was a faint click in his earphones. Just as his squadron leader started to give the order to make the turn, Mikhandi Lal's plane gave a sudden, quick shudder. It began to nosedive. Every second the dive steepened. Below, the dark green jungle was beginning to show crystal clear. Not just a blur of green, but patches of green with a narrow river winding its way down the hillside.

The MIG's controls felt as if they had been bolted into position. Mikhandi Lal exerted all his strength on them, but could not get the slightest movement. Again he glanced at the instrument panel.

Vaguely in his earphones he heard his squadron leader's voice: "Mikhandi Lal, if you are out of control, bail out! Don't wait. Bail out now! Are you hearing me, Lieutenant Lal?"

The young Indian pilot knew what he had to do. Dragging down his face mask and holding it with his left hand, he depressed the ejector control with a quick thrust of his right hand. He was barely ejected from the plane when a tremendous rush of air knocked him unconscious. His parachute opened automatically.

In the jungle below there was a sudden blossoming of dark-colored smoke where the MIG had crashed and exploded. Three thousand feet above, Mikhandi Lal knew nothing of that. Had he been conscious, he might have been able to guide his chute and reach the earth with no more than a few bruises. Instead, he struck the treetops.

Birds flew screaming as he hit the branches and slithered through to the earth below. Limbs creaked under his weight. Twigs broke off. Then there was the hiss of the tearing parachute. The last sound was the softest of thuds when he crumpled up in a tiny clearing. After that there was silence—if the jungle is ever silent.

Mikhandi Lal groped his way painfully back to consciousness. He was badly bruised. The real damage, however, was to one of his legs. There was something strange about the way it was twisted under him. Yet for a little while he hardly realized how serious was the damage. His left hand was badly bruised. There was a lump on his forehead. But it was the darkness, growing quickly deep, that frightened him.

Painfully, his memory came back. He felt a cold chill of fear as he realized that he had come down in the jungle. He had flown over it many times, but had never set foot in it. He had listened to lectures on survival. He had listened and made notes, but somehow the idea that he could crash in the jungle had never occurred to him. To others, yes, but not to him.

He sat for some time, hoping his aching head would stop pounding. Gradually he realized that he was listening. People talk of the silence of the night, but there was no silence here. There were sounds—some near, some far away. He began to have the feeling that hidden eyes were staring at him.

The ache in his right leg finally took his mind off the many little noises of the night. Though he was half afraid to touch his leg, he was at least able to get it into a better position. He fainted twice before he was able to drag himself to a tree.

With his back to the trunk, he felt safer. After a few minutes he remembered the survival kit. It was a small tin that he kept in a special pocket in his flying uniform. Carefully he pawed through the contents.

The little package of chocolate squares helped him to a more cheerful frame of mind. Chewing one of the tiny

310

squares reminded him of the canteen at the airfield. That made him think of his squadron leader. He would know where the MIG had crashed, and by morning he would have rescue operations under way. Mikhandi Lal felt better. He tried to sleep. It was an uneasy night of catnapping and trying to keep his leg in the least painful position.

An hour before daylight the dew began to form on the leaves of the trees. Soon the quiet was broken by a succession of plops as water gathered to the lowest part of a leaf, then dripped off. The sound would have been frightening if Mikhandi Lal had heard it, for the plops somehow sounded like the pattering of tiny feet.

When he did wake up, his heart was pounding wildly, and there was gooseflesh on his cheeks. He sat up, feeling a sharp pain in his leg and wondering what the strange call was that had wakened him. Seconds later it came again: a high-pitched *cock-a-doodle!*

Less than ten feet away a jungle cock was stretching his neck and pointing his head to the sky. He challenged the morning with another *cock-a-doodle!* Within a minute there seemed to be scores of jungle cocks answering the challenge. Dawn was coming. The grayness changed quickly, and suddenly a warm light was shining through the tops of the trees. The new day had come.

By this time the little cock—a dashing beauty in red, green, and vivid black and standing no more than nine inches high—had been joined by some hens. They had fluttered down from the branches of the surrounding trees and were scratching among the dead leaves. Another hen came from beneath the low-growing branches of a nearby bush. At her soft clucking a dozen chicks pattered out to join her. It was a scene of peace, with the hens scratching away and the chicks pushing in to look for ants and tiny grubs.

Mikhandi Lal watched and tried to forget his utter weariness and the ache in his right leg. He knew the bone was broken. The pain was like the throb-throb-throb of a bass drum. He had lain so still that neither the cock nor any of the hens seemed to have noticed he was there.

Suddenly the scene changed. There was an urgent *tuk-tuk-tuk* from the cock followed by a frantic whirring of wings. The hens fluttered upward to the safety of high branches. The hen with the chicks also gave her orders in an urgent, low clucking as she hurried to the hidden nest under the bushes.

Mikhandi Lal had been half asleep when the commotion brought him back to wakefulness. A single brown feather floated down from a hen settling on a branch up above. In the clearing there was one little ball of fluff. A chick had not followed its mother to the safety of the nest. Instead, the little chick was busy investigating an ant struggling to drag a dead insect. The hen came again, clucking urgently.

Mikhandi Lal wondered what the commotion was about. Within seconds the reason was plain. A snake glided into view, its scaly body making a slight rustling sound on the leaves. The young pilot was city born and knew little or nothing about snakes. Yet he had a sudden, cold sense of fear at the sight of this one. He would have been even more alarmed had he known that it was a king

cobra, one of the deadliest snakes in India. It is the one snake that will attack a person without cause.

It came on without hesitation, its cold, jewel eyes fixed on the chick that had heard too late its mother's urgent warning clucks. Too frightened to move, the chick crouched down in the leaves, as though hoping the danger would pass by if it remained still.

Mikhandi Lal watched with little interest. Pain and shock seemed to have robbed him of the desire to do anything. Even the thought that search parties might already be on their way scarcely raised a flicker of hope. The jungle was vast and thick. The chances of being found were a million to one.

His eyelids were closing when a sudden squawking and a wild flutter of wings made him look up. The mother hen had left her nest and was trying to draw the cobra away from her chick. With one wing dragging, as if it were broken, she scuttled to within a few feet of the cobra. Squawking, she tried to get it to follow her.

The chance of an even better meal tempted the cobra. It made a lightning lunge at the hen. Had the blow found its target, the hen would have died instantly. Somehow she was able to evade the blow.

Twice more she scuttled temptingly in front of the cobra. Twice more she barely escaped death. Mikhandi Lal sat upright, amazed at such courage, and hoping the hen would be able to save her chick. But the next time she came temptingly close to the cobra, she received a glancing blow that rolled her over and over. Squawking in terror, she darted into the bushes. She had done all she could. She had other chicks to protect.

The cobra lowered its head to begin a second attack, and Mikhandi Lal was filled with sudden anger. He looked around for something to throw. It seemed wrong that the brave little hen should not be rewarded.

Before he could pick up a piece of broken branch, there was still another attempt to save the chick. This time it was made by the jungle cock, coming down from the safety of the tree for a do-or-die attack. With an incredible display of bravery, he checked his flight within inches of the cobra's head. He jabbed down with his needle-sharp spurs. Though he missed the unwinking eyes, he drew two pinpoints of blood.

"Go on . . . go on!" Mikhandi Lal forgot his own ordeal in his desire for the cobra to be beaten off. The unexpected sound of a human voice distracted the cobra. A sudden swing of its head—which might well have dashed the jungle cock to the ground—missed the target.

The cock swept in again, his wings fluttering with amazing speed. The cobra swayed its powerful body to keep away from the sharp spurs. The little cock jabbed again and again. He drew blood once more, but missed his target, which was the cobra's eyes.

A few moments later the cock paid for his bold attack. The cobra struck a glancing blow that sent his feathers flying. The blow was a heavy one, and the cock was flung yards away, where he lay with one wing outstretched.

Hissing with anger, the cobra slithered across to finish off the cock. This was too much for Mikhandi Lal. Pulling himself onto one knee, the young pilot grabbed the rotting branch he had noted earlier. He flung it wildly across the clearing.

The aim was good. However, the branch was so rotten that it broke as it struck the cobra. The branch saved the cock, but it brought immediate trouble for Mikhandi Lal. He watched in horror as the cobra hurled about and raced toward him, hissing like a leaky kettle.

This was a full-grown cobra, some twelve feet long. Its head and almost half its body reared above the ground. It seemed to tower above Mikhandi Lal. Then suddenly it began a strange, frightening, swaying motion.

Mikhandi Lal stared upward, trying to think what to do and unable to move because of his injured leg.

As the swaying motion began to slow he reached for another branch. With one sweeping movement, he tossed it up. At that short distance he could hardly miss.

The cobra's head swayed sideways, then came down in what should have been a paralyzing punch. But the thrown branch had unbalanced the cobra, so that it struck Mikhandi Lal where his arm and shoulder joined. The blow was like a kick and, spinning him sideways, threw him down. The cobra also fell forward, flopping to the ground within feet of its intended victim.

Mikhandi Lal had forgotten his injured leg, his pain, his exhaustion. With a resounding shriek, he began to roll away, out of reach. The cobra also moved, now quicker, surer. Its head reared up and a moment later was towering over Mikhandi Lal, ready for another attempt to finish him off.

There was no feeling of despair about the young pilot now. His fear had given way to anger. He knew that the cobra was ready to strike again. Lying with his arms out-stretched, he groped in the leaves for a stone, a stick — anything with which he could hit back at this cold-eyed killer. But there was nothing, only dead leaves that crumbled to dust under his grasp.

Realizing the cobra had stopped hissing and swaying, Mikhandi Lal nerved himself for a last attempt to evade death. Every muscle tense, he was ready to lunge to one side. Then he heard a pitiful little *cheep-cheep-cheep!* The chick that had been the cause of all this commotion was lying half smothered under part of the cobra's scaly tail.

Within seconds, the whole situation changed.

The jungle cock, who had struggled to his feet, was trying to shake his crumpled feathers smooth. A moment later he was flying at the cobra in a fury of fast-beating wings.

In the very act of starting to strike at Mikhandi Lal, the cobra automatically turned to meet the attack. The cock did not try to jab with his spurs, but drove in with his beak.

From where he lay on the ground, Mikhandi Lal saw the shortest battle ever. The cock struck and a moment later was flung yards away. He rolled over on the leaf-covered ground and started to give a defiant little *cock-a-doodle.* He never finished his challenge. His wings relaxed, and he lay quivering for a moment.

The cobra seemed to go mad. Forgetful of the man on the ground, it hurled itself about. Then suddenly it turned and glided away, looking for some hiding place where it could be safe until it could see again. It was blinded in one eye and for the time being could not see from the other one. The jungle has no mercy on the weak or the injured. The snake had to seek shelter.

Silence for a few moments, then another pitiful *cheep-cheep-cheep.* The mother hen came out and scratched at the leaves in which her youngster was half hidden. Then she hustled the chick away to the safety of the bushes.

After waiting for a minute or so, Mikhandi Lal sat up, shaking from head to foot. When he finally calmed down, he dragged himself to the little bundle of vividly colored feathers. Only a short time before, it had been a brave jungle cock. Mikhandi Lal struggled back to the tree, carrying the dead cock gently in his right hand.

"What courage," he whispered, stroking the crumpled feathers to smoothness. "What magnificent courage!" He sat stroking the feathered back for several minutes. He looked down at his injured leg. Until the cobra had come on the scene, he had been ready to lie there and die. Despair had gripped him. Now he laid the cock down. He pulled himself up on his sound leg and looked for something to help him walk.

When the search parties found Lieutenant Lal later that afternoon, he had somehow struggled through the jungle to a clearing. The smoke from his fire had caught the eye of a helicopter pilot. From that moment rescue was assured.

"What's this you've got?" The doctor at the base touched a limp bundle of vividly colored feathers tied to Mikhandi Lal's belt.

"That's courage. Just courage," was the shaky reply. "Look after him. I want him — always."

The doctor thought the pilot was light-headed after his ordeal. And there were a number of raised eyebrows when Mikhandi Lal asked that the little jungle cock be taken to a taxidermist and stuffed.

Some weeks later, standing proudly in an airtight case, the little cock was placed on the wall in Mikhandi's quarters. By then, of course, everybody knew the story of the fighting jungle cock. Only to a very close friend did the young pilot explain why he wanted to keep the cock. "It's just to remind me — especially when things go wrong — that nothing is too big to tackle, if you have courage.

"The taxidermist told me the cock weighed twelve ounces. Just twelve ounces of unbroken courage."

# ASHU AND THE WHIRLWIND

## by Erick Berry

Ashu was a daughter of the Jukons, once a mighty nation of warriors and priests in West Africa. She often thought with pride of her nation and of her tribe, but she was only thirteen years old, and sometimes other things seemed more important.

Just now Ashu stood in the little mud house that was her home. She held a tiny mirror in her hand, trying to see in it the whole of her face. But when she saw one bright eye, the other disappeared from the little mirror. And when she saw her wide-lipped mouth with its flashing teeth, her small black nose was out of the picture. She tried hardest of all to see the orange headcloth, folded into a long flat piece and tied around her head like a turban. The ends were left flapping over one earringed ear, and her curly hair stuck up through the center.

She made a face at herself in the mirror. A cotton headcloth! Ashu, daughter of the Jukons, longed for silk. She had seen a certain silk handkerchief hanging in the booth of a trader in the market. She had cast longing eyes on it only yesterday, and the day before, and the day before that. It was a rich orange brocade patterned with magenta—truly a wonderful headcloth. But it cost ten shillings, and she did not have ten shillings!

She went again to the marketplace, the center of life
of every African town. Men from the hills, clad only in
breechcloths, were in sharp contrast to the chiefs of the
district, who wore flowing white robes and huge spotless
turbans. The smell of lemon oil mingled with the odors
of dried fish and of freshly killed meat.

Ashu pressed through the market-day crowd, turning her back on the booth where the orange handkerchief hung. A storyteller was beating a drum in one corner of the market, at the same time keeping up an endless folk-tale to amuse the crowd. Ashu joined the group but with only half an ear for the story.

Close to her stood two traders, talking quietly. Without meaning to listen, she heard their remarks above the drumming of the storyteller.

". . . Amadu, the thief they call the Whirlwind, is in Wukari."

The Whirlwind! What a curious name! thought Ashu, and pressed closer that she might hear better above the beating of the storyteller's drum.

The first trader, a tall man clad in a long blue robe, continued. "A large reward is offered for Amadu's capture, but the risk in taking him would be great. He has a charm that carries evil. All people know of it. His first wife made it for him, and Allah struck her with blindness. The charm is wicked beyond belief."

The shorter man gave a grunt of interest.

"This charm," went on the other, "he still has, and there is no charm to oppose it. I myself would like the reward, but I also value my life."

Just then the two men moved off, still talking.

Ashu noted that the full moon was slowly rising through the trees, its bright light in sharp contrast to the dark sky. Very thoughtfully she turned her back on the market and wandered away. Who was this Amadu whom they called the Whirlwind?

Now she heard the sound of drumming in another part of the town and hastened toward it. Some young people were grouped about two native drummers. They were dancing and shouting and clapping. Anyone who wished might join the dance.

Ashu tightened the cloth about her hips, gave an extra twist to her headcloth, and stepped into the dance. Slowly the full moon rose. The red dust beat up from the hard-packed earth. The voices of singers rose and fell, and Ashu danced on and on.

It was nearing daylight, and the moon was about to set when the dancers began to drift away to their huts. Ashu, still not tired, was among the last to leave.

The town was never quite deserted at night, never wholly asleep. Ashu, having said her good nights in a high sweet voice, ran swiftly down the street. The moon was low now, and the street was dark. Ahead of her was a stranger, also moving quickly. She had noticed him some time before as he stood watching the dancers from the shadow of a tree. He had a rapid walk, almost catlike, and the girl wondered who he might be. Her own feet made no sound on the dusty way.

Suddenly the stranger darted down the narrow opening into the small alley that led to Ashu's own house. As he turned he gave a quick glance behind him. Ashu's figure melted into the black shadow of the high wall, and he did not see her. She was close behind him now, and she saw him dodge quickly into the entrance of her father's compound. Suddenly remembering what she had heard earlier about a thief, Ashu also remembered that her father kept a heavy money box buried deep in the earth floor behind the entrance hut.

"Thou!" she called loudly, and rushed in after the man. She saw the figure turn as she came up. She made a grab

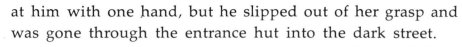

at him with one hand, but he slipped out of her grasp and was gone through the entrance hut into the dark street.

One might as well try to catch a whirlwind. Whirlwind! This must be Amadu, the Whirlwind! Now she understood the reason for the name. The girl turned and went on into the compound slowly, thoughtfully.

On the following Friday, Gaddo, her father, who was a worker in leather, said that he planned to start for Ibi two days later for a trading trip. Ashu decided to stay at home with the younger children. But the older women in the compound thought that they would go with Gaddo. The hairdresser in Ibi was known to be very good, and it was many weeks since they had had their hair dressed.

Thirty miles for a new hairdressing, then back again in a day or two—that was just a pleasure trip to an African native. On moonlit nights the roads were busy with an endless stream of travelers and traders. They came from other districts, from across the desert, from the snowy mountains, and from the jungles, always trading, always moving onward.

When the family had gone, Ashu went back to the compound and made her plans. She was frightened, but excited and interested. If the man she had seen was the Whirlwind, he would come again. No doubt he would hear of the family trip and take advantage of it.

Cleverly, she managed that evening to coax some girls who had started dancing in the next street to come into the compound of her own house. The dance lasted very late. When the drummers finally left, some of the girls stayed on eating mangoes, telling stories, and chattering till daylight. No thief would enter as long as they were there.

It was late the next morning when Ashu hastened to market with a plan in the back of her head.

When she reached the marketplace, she joined a group of men who sat talking in the shade of one of the small market booths. Among them was her uncle Ablus, who was her father's brother and a police officer of Wukari. As the morning was hot, he had taken off his heavy red turban. It lay behind him, along with his red cotton shoulder band and the handcuffs Ashu needed for her plan.

She crept into the shade and sat down next to Ablus. He gave her a smile, patted her hand, and went on talking with the other men. Half an hour later, when Ashu got up to leave, he did not even look up. So he did not know that the handcuffs lay in the bottom of her calabash beneath some corn she was carrying.

That evening Ashu did not feel nearly so brave as she had felt earlier. It was all very well to plan in broad daylight to catch a thief and to work all day to set a trap for him. It was another thing to wait at night with a pounding heart, in the dark stillness of a little entrance hut, to carry out the plan. Her mouth was dry. Her knees were shaking. She lay down on the mat that she had dragged from her own hut and pretended to be asleep.

Before long she heard a slight sound. She peered out from beneath her arm. Surely a shadow had crossed the moonlight in the doorway.

She was right. Someone was beginning to dig, softly, in the place just inside the compound wall. Ashu, her heart starting to pound all over again, gave a little sigh, intending it to be heard.

It had hardly been uttered before the Whirlwind, living up to his name, was beside her. He laid a heavy hand on her mouth.

"Who is that?" he asked sharply. Then, realizing that it was only a child, he lifted his hand that she might reply, but he kept a rough hold on her shoulder.

"I am Ashu, the daughter of Gaddo!" she answered, and struggled to sit up.

There was silence for a moment. Then a voice demanded, "Are you alone in the compound?"

"There is no one else here but the small children," said Ashu.

The Whirlwind's hand slipped from her shoulder, and Ashu's courage began to come back. Perhaps her plan might work after all.

"Come!" ordered the thief in a whisper. "Show me the place where the silver is hidden."

His hand pulled her toward the wall where, indeed, the money was buried. He let go her wrist and pressed a sharp knife against her side.

"Dig!" he ordered in a low voice. "You know where. Let the work be swift."

Ashu had no intention of opposing the Whirlwind's order. Her hands found the small jungle knife with which he had started to dig up the earth. Pretending to work swiftly, Ashu nevertheless took her time. Meanwhile the knife pressed unpleasantly against her side and pressed even closer when the sound of voices came from the street.

Ashu pushed at the loose earth with swift brown hands, and the Whirlwind, eager and quick, soon laid down the knife to help.

Ashu dug deeper and deeper. The moon rose higher and higher. At last she felt the touch of cold iron, down an arm's length into the cool earth.

"Here is what you seek," she said.

"Where?" asked the Whirlwind. "Show me!"

His hand was on her wrist, and she guided it down, down in the darkness. There was a little gasp from him as he felt the iron.

"You'll need both hands," she suggested. "It's all in an iron box, one of the white people's boxes. It is very heavy." Her arm was still in the hole, while he was stretched out beside her, trying to reach both hands after hers. Roughly he pushed her aside.

"Let me be. I will do it alone," he said.

But Ashu's hand was still guiding his. Suddenly there was the sound of a metal click. Ashu sprang up.

Amadu, the Whirlwind, lay face down, his arms in the hole. His wrists were held tightly by the handcuffs Ashu had that afternoon fastened to the handle of the heavy iron box. Her plan had worked!

Hugging herself with delight, the girl ran through the streets in the moonlight, straight to the house of her uncle. She went to tell him where he could find his handcuffs.

It was a week later. Ashu peered into her little mirror admiringly. On top of her curly hair was a splendid silk handkerchief of flaming orange patterned with magenta. She had received a good reward for the capture of the Whirlwind in the very act of robbing her father. She patted the handkerchief happily.

# The Incredible
# Answer-Before-the-Question Trick

by Marilyn Burns

This is not a trick for the fainthearted.
If there are any people in your audience who can't stand
the shock of a truly astounding experience,
you had better ask them to leave the room now.
For in this trick you will
GIVE THE ANSWER BEFORE THE QUESTION!
And it will be the right answer.

| | | |
|---|---|---|
| Look as though you are concentrating very hard. Write the number 1,089 on a piece of paper.  | Show the number to one person and say: "Here is the answer. Keep it, but do not reveal the answer."  | Announce in a grand voice: "There is the answer. Now I need a question."  |
| Choose another person from the audience.  | Tell that person: "Write down a number with 3 different digits."  | Now say: "Reverse the digits. Subtract the smaller number from the larger number. What is your answer?"  |

| Continue: "Write the answer. Reverse the digits. Add both numbers." | The total will always be 1,089! (If you subtract and add correctly) | Ask both persons to compare their answers and then tell the audience . . . |
|---|---|---|

$$\begin{array}{r} 495 \\ +594 \\ \hline 1,089 \end{array}$$

1,089

. . . but don't tell how you did the trick. If your audience is stumped and you have to do it again, there's a good chance someone will begin to see the pattern. So only do that trick once! Be sure to choose people who can add and subtract.

Beware of numbers whose first and last digits differ by only 1. If such a number is given, call for a different one. If that doesn't work, think of something astounding to say, like: "I have to go now." Then make your exit.

I can't figure it out!

Write a 3-digit number whose first and last digits
differ by only 1.
Reverse the first and last digits.
Subtract.
What is your answer?
Does the trick work? Why or why not?

# Exploring Crystals

by James Berry

The accident happened just as the sun's slanting rays beamed into the Paris house where Abbé Haüy sat deep in thought.

For years, Abbé Haüy had spent most of his time studying the characteristics of minerals. Now, in the book-lined room, he looked at a rare specimen that a friend had given him. It was a six-inch-long piece of the mineral calcite. Abbé Haüy was especially interested in this mineral.

Carefully, he took the piece of calcite and turned it in his long, slender fingers, noting its size and shape. Then, somehow, it slipped from his hand and fell to the floor, where it splintered into three large fragments.

Abbé Haüy sighed. The year was 1781, and the best specimens of this particular mineral came from Iceland, first brought by boat, then carried over dirt roads to Paris. Such a large piece of calcite had been hard to obtain. Getting another like it might take months.

The Abbé might not have been so disappointed had he known that the three fragments would help him answer an important question. This question had puzzled scientists for centuries: What is solid matter made of?

Gently, he picked up the largest fragment. It was about three inches long and had six flat sides that met in sharp corners. It had a pointed top and a bottom that flared out into something like a pyramid. It was an odd shape, and one too regular to have been formed by chance. In addition, the fragment was symmetrical. If it were cut in two from tip to base, each half would look exactly like the other half.

This many-sided, symmetrical piece of calcite was a crystal.

Then, Abbé Haüy noticed the second-largest fragment. His forehead wrinkled into a puzzled frown. This piece of broken calcite was smaller than the first. But its shape was exactly the same.

Abbé Haüy reached for the third fragment. It was only a half inch or so long, much smaller than the first two pieces. Its shape was identical to that of the other two pieces. Abbé Haüy realized that he had made an important discovery.

*quartz*

*cerussite*

*phlogopite*

*stibnite*

The calcite crystal had splintered into three identically shaped pieces. Each piece was shaped like a pyramid, each one smaller than the next. Now, Abbé Haüy wondered if these crystals could be divided into yet smaller ones.

At first, he used a sharp knife to carefully split the smallest crystal into smaller crystals. When the smallest crystal became too tiny to handle, the Abbé used his imagination to divide it into smaller units. Eventually, Abbé Haüy decided, he would reach the smallest possible unit. And, he realized, it is millions of such units, stacked in orderly rows, that form large crystals.

Other solid matter is also made of crystals. For instance, ice cubes, icicles, and snowflakes are made of crystals so tiny they can hardly be seen. So, too, are the grains of sand on your beaches, the metals in bridges, coins, and rings.

Even stones are made of crystals. The weather has usually polished the stones so smooth that the crystals are hard to see. But, with a magnifying glass, hundreds of tiny crystals, closely packed, can often be seen in a recently broken stone.

*snowflake*

*galena*

Perhaps the most fascinating characteristic of crystals is the regular shapes they form. Salt crystals are cubes. Pour a few grains of salt onto a table and study them through a magnifying glass. In most cases, the crystals will be nicked or chipped because the grains of salt have rubbed against one another. But a few grains should still be perfect cubes. Salt crystals have a simple shape. Other kinds of crystals have complex shapes and beautiful colors. Perhaps that is why Abbé Haüy called crystals the "flowers of the mineral kingdom."

Some crystals look like two pyramids placed base to base. Others look like long, slender needles. Still others are flat with only a few sides, or tall and thick with many sides. Some crystals are a pale blue, green, or yellow. Others are dark brown, purple, red, or orange. In many cases, crystals are as clear as glass.

Since Abbé Haüy's time, the study of crystals has helped scientists understand many of the mysteries of solid matter.

Today, the study of crystals has led to many new discoveries, and scientists are studying solid matter more intensely than ever before. The end is nowhere in sight.

*staurolite*

*sulfur*

*tourmaline*

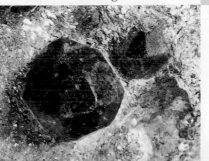

*copper*

*vanadinite*          *almandine garnet*

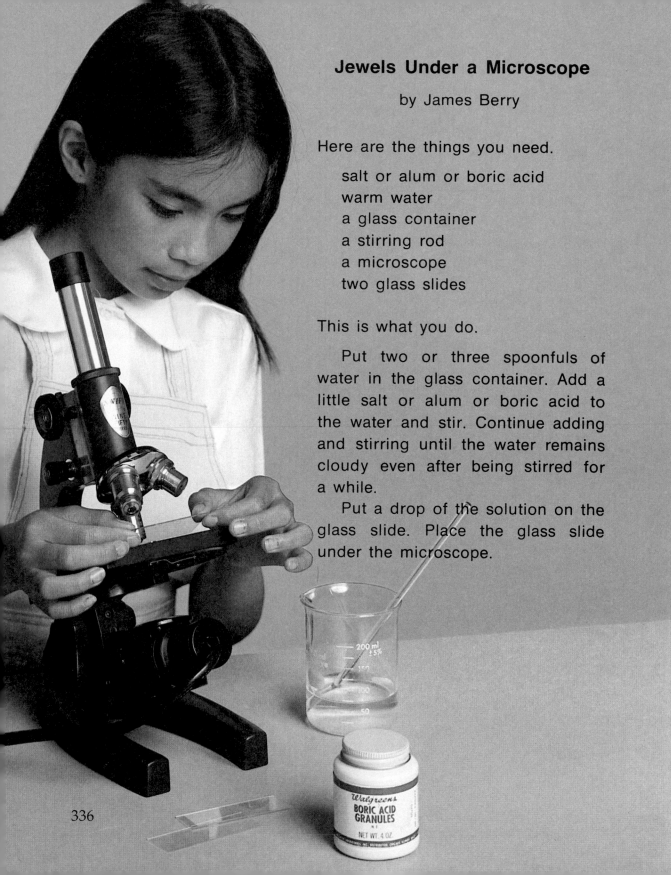

# Jewels Under a Microscope

## by James Berry

Here are the things you need.

salt or alum or boric acid
warm water
a glass container
a stirring rod
a microscope
two glass slides

This is what you do.

Put two or three spoonfuls of water in the glass container. Add a little salt or alum or boric acid to the water and stir. Continue adding and stirring until the water remains cloudy even after being stirred for a while.

Put a drop of the solution on the glass slide. Place the glass slide under the microscope.

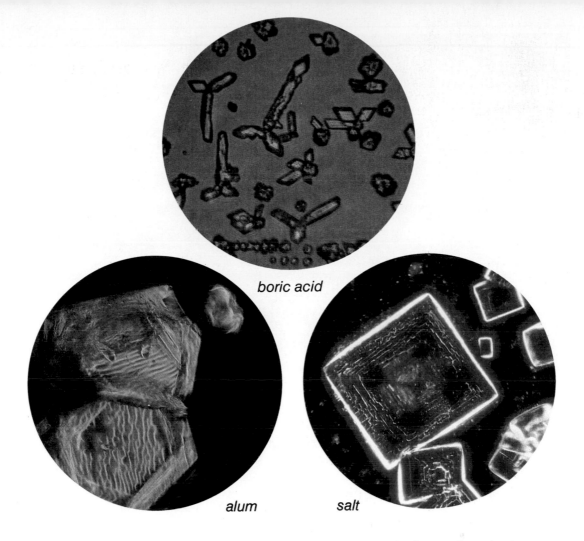

*boric acid*

*alum*     *salt*

As the water evaporates from the solution, tiny but beautifully shaped crystals will begin to form at the edge of the drop. As more water evaporates, new crystals may seem to sprout from the center of the drop, as if by magic.

Try making crystals a second time by placing a drop of the solution on the other slide. This time blow on the drop to make it evaporate more rapidly. The crystals will begin to form. Compare the size of these crystals with the size of those that grew naturally.

# THE HUNT
# FOR THE MASTODON

by Georgianne Ensign

It was a giant tooth. No doubt about that. Sticking out of the brown mud of the embankment, it was half as long as a football. It was yellowed with age and at first had looked like the sort of animal bone that occasionally turns up in someone's garden. But on closer examination the two boys had no difficulty in seeing what it was. They could hardly believe their eyes! What was a giant tooth like that doing here?

John Versace and Jimmy DiFranco had found it quite accidentally one cold Wednesday in January, 1962. The boys had been testing ice for skating in some large ditches behind their homes on land that belonged to Jimmy's father. The ditches had been formed by the construction of a huge highway three hundred feet above their heads. The highway was thrusting its way through their town straight to the George Washington Bridge and New York City. John and Jimmy lived in Hackensack, New Jersey, a city with an old Indian name, and the capital of Bergen County. They were so close to New York City that on most days they could see the tallest skyscrapers from their backyards.

As they were walking along, the boys had seen a yellowish object in the dirt. It looked like stone, but a closer look revealed something far more exciting. It was an enormous tooth. To their amazement, they soon discovered two more mysterious teeth lying on the ground nearby. The teeth were long and smooth on each side. They looked like human teeth, except they were much larger. And there were six conelike bumps, placed in two rows of three on the top of each tooth.

Putting the teeth in a line on the ground, the boys tried to picture the size of the jaw from which they had come. It must have been huge! Surely the teeth belonged to some prehistoric monster.

The boys took the teeth home and gave them a good washing. The next day they brought them eagerly to their junior-high-school science teacher, Richard Straubel. Strangely enough, he had given the class a lecture only two days before, advising what to do if they ever found anything scientifically interesting.

From the size of the teeth, Straubel knew that they were unique. He also noticed that they were beginning to crumble when they were handled. He told the boys that it was important to get the teeth to an expert as quickly as possible. They were really excited when he telephoned the American Museum of Natural History in New York and was advised to bring the finds in for examination.

But that was only the beginning. The next day Jimmy, John, and Mr. Straubel found themselves in the museum, feeling very special. There were thousands of visitors who were flocking to see the dinosaurs or the true-to-life animal exhibits. But the boys and their teacher were going behind the scenes, past the cases of exhibits that the public is allowed to see. They had special reasons to be there—reasons they carried with them, carefully wrapped in two boxes.

They stopped at a door that was labeled *Department of Vertebrate Paleontology*. Mr. Straubel explained that vertebrate paleontology is the study of the fossil remains of backboned animals that no longer exist. The department's curator was Dr. Edwin H. Colbert, one of the world's most outstanding paleontologists. He was the man they had come to see.

Dr. Colbert was waiting for them. As soon as he had met the boys and their teacher, he asked to see the finds they were holding in their arms.

The boys carefully unwrapped the teeth they had just as carefully packed in their boxes. Dr. Colbert picked up the teeth one by one and examined them thoroughly. He wanted to know everything about them. He asked where the boys had found the teeth and whether they had marked the spot. He asked them if they had seen any other bones in the area. He wanted to know whether they had treated the teeth with any kind of preservative.

The boys told him the whole story. After Dr. Colbert examined the teeth some more, he had them treated with a preservative. This would prevent them from cracking and crumbling. He explained that fossils begin to disintegrate when they are suddenly exposed to air.

Preserving fossils is important to paleontologists, because a fossil is a clue to the mystery of the past. It is mostly through studying fossils that scientists have been able to piece together what they know about prehistoric times.

Dr. Colbert was especially concerned about two things. One was that none of Jimmy and John's friends would go looking for treasure before the museum experts could get to the spot. The other was that the bulldozers that were clearing the land for the highway would not damage any other remains that might still be there.

Dr. Colbert also told the boys some interesting information. Curious as it may seem, he said, many prehistoric finds are unearthed by people in their struggle for modern improvement. The prehistoric teeth had been found because a new highway was being built. Many Indian treasures are found when farmers plow their fields with modern equipment.

It was interesting, all right, but the boys were eager to learn more about what they had found. Dr. Colbert decided that the easiest way was to show them. He led them through the museum until they stood in front of a huge wall painting.

What the painting seemed to show was just an elephant with long, curved tusks. This was disappointing, because the boys had been picturing a *Tyrannosaurus* — the greatest dinosaur — at least.

But Dr. Colbert quickly assured them that this was not *just* an elephant. What they found were the teeth of an American mastodon. This mastodon, a prehistoric cousin of the modern elephant, had lived in the United States about ten thousand years earlier.

The boys took another look.

Dr. Colbert told them that the mastodon was shorter and heavier than its modern cousin, the African elephant. It had a flatter head and gracefully curved tusks that grew as long as six feet.

The modern African elephant is about eleven feet tall. The American mastodon, however, was probably only nine feet tall. It had long, brownish-red hair. That was just the warm kind of coat the mastodon needed, because it lived in the great Ice Age. During that time of arctic cold, huge waves of ice and snow moved down over much of North America. The ice reached as far south as the present state of Pennsylvania. New Jersey itself was a vast tundra, a frozen, treeless wasteland. Then slowly, as the ice moved northward again, there grew new forests of pine and hemlock on which the mastodons fed. Scientists believe, said Dr. Colbert, that a bridge of land connected Asia and North America. Somehow the mastodons found their way across this land bridge. Near the end of the Ice Age, they became extinct.

As Dr. Colbert talked, he led the boys and Mr. Straubel through the big exhibition hall. Finally they stood in front of a row of giant elephantlike skeletons. From these, with a little help, the boys were able to pick out a mastodon. It was truly magnificent, and they regarded it with considerable respect. They found themselves looking first at its huge curved tusks, and then at its teeth. They compared what they had found with what they saw.

Sure enough, there were the same conelike bumps on the top of each tooth. Dr. Colbert told them that these

bumps distinguished the mastodon from its African cousin, whose teeth are flat on the chewing surface. It was lucky, he said, that the boys had found the teeth instead of a piece of bone. For it was the teeth that helped him identify at once what they had discovered.

"Too bad you didn't find the animal whole," he teased them, and they all laughed.

When John and Jimmy left the museum, they were quite excited about their discovery and Dr. Colbert's interest in it. They had agreed to give the fossils to the Bergen Community Museum, so that other people could share their find. Dr. Colbert had promised in turn to visit John and Jimmy's junior high school to talk to the students about the mastodon.

At home, the boys found they had become heroes overnight. The local newspapers had written stories about them. One story told how John's mother had warned the boys not to dirty her sink when they brought the teeth home to wash them. Jimmy's classmates were now calling him "Biology Joe." And John's classmates were calling him "the dinosaur-teeth finder."

With such excitement afoot it was asking too much of them to stay away from the discovery site. And within a week they had done it again! A few feet from the spot where they had found the first teeth they found another tooth with the same distinguishing conelike bumps. Then they discovered part of a bone—a large one. After a bit of investigation the boys left it where they found it. Scientists from the American Museum of Natural History came to the site and identified the bone as part of a lower jaw. In trying to uncover the bone, Jimmy had accidentally knocked a tooth off the jaw. Now the men covered the bone again and left it in the ground. It was to wait there throughout the remaining months of the winter.

Dr. Colbert decided that with so much evidence at hand it would be wise to try to find the rest of the skeleton. If it was there, it would be worth the cost of excavation.

"It's possible that the whole skeleton is there. We've just got to take that chance," he said.

Unfortunately, the weather was cold and the ground was frozen. It would be difficult to take the bones out of the earth without their cracking and chipping. For that reason the excavation was put off until spring. Dr. Colbert asked the boys to discontinue their digging until then, when they could have the help of experts.

It was not until March 30, more than two months after the teeth were discovered, that the digging began. On that day, the boys watched George Whitaker uncover the same lower jaw that they had helped cover with earth in January. George Whitaker was a laboratory technician at the American Museum of Natural History. His job included the entire process of excavating and preparing fossils for display.

His digging techniques surprised the boys, who crouched nearby to watch him work. Carefully he flicked away pieces of dirt from the jaw, working with tools that looked like instruments a dentist might use. In fact, some of them were. As each small piece of bone was exposed, Whitaker whisked away the crumbling earth with a soft camel's-hair brush. It was a delicate process and took a lot of patience. But the bone was also delicate. One false move could chip or crumble it. The moisture in the earth had protected the bone , but it would begin to disintegrate when it was uncovered and exposed to the air.

Once a bone was completely uncovered, Whitaker painted it with a chemical solution to preserve it.

After applying the chemical solution, he covered the entire bone with strips of wet newspaper. Then he made a cast for the bone, using a solution of plaster of Paris

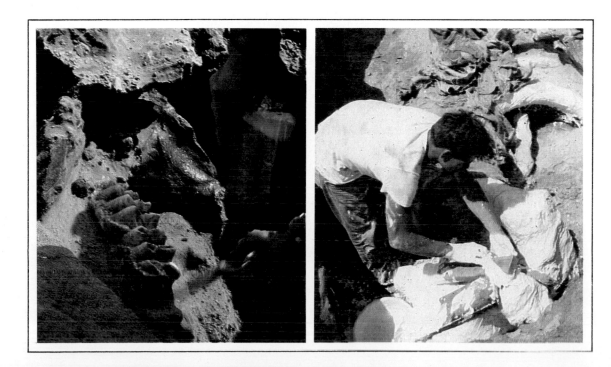

and strips of burlap. Whitaker made the cast in the same way a doctor makes a cast for a broken leg. One by one, the strips of burlap were dipped into the plaster and laid on the wet paper. Then the cast was allowed to dry and harden.

Once the bone was inside the cast, it could be crated and carried safely to the museum in New York.

In November the dig was closed down for the year. Most of the bones of the mastodon had been found with the exception of the legs. When the excavation began again the following spring, there was still no trace of the mastodon's legs.

Finally, in June, the site excavators called an end to the dig. They stood and watched as a tractor filled the pit with dirt. The dig had meant so much to the excavators that the moment was a sad one.

Still, it was not the end. The work would continue in the laboratory of the American Museum of Natural History. There the mastodon bones would be prepared for display.

Because the leg bones had not been found, the scientists decided they would not put the rest of the skeleton together. Instead, Whitaker would make a new kind of exhibit for the Bergen Community Museum. It would show how the mastodon looked as it was found in the ground.

The museum technicians prepared a display that looked much like the actual scene of the dig. In the exhibit were placed the bones of the mastodon, as well as the bones of some smaller animals that were found.

The result was amazingly natural. Working in his spare time at the museum, George Whitaker had taken two years to complete the exhibit. But it was worth the time and the patience he put into it.

Thousands of people have seen the mastodon in the Bergen Community Museum. But the story of the Hackensack mastodon is a mystery. How did the mastodon come to die? What happened to its leg bones? Why did the mastodons become extinct? These are questions for which there are no final answers—questions that perhaps another hunt for another mastodon may help to answer.

And what was the value of the peculiar teeth that John Versace and Jimmy DiFranco had found that cold January day, practically in their own backyards?

The boys had found a tiny clue to a past age that is still vastly unknown. Their discovery added to the existing scientific evidence that mastodons lived and died on this land. What is important is that through the awareness of two young boys, one more fragment of the earth's history was saved from destruction.

### Dinosaurs

Their feet, planted into tar,
drew them down,
back to the core of birth,
and all they are
is found in earth,
recovered, bone by bone,
rising again, like stone
skeletons, naked, white,
to live again, staring,
head holes glaring,
towering, proud, tall,
in some museum hall.

Myra Cohn Livingston

Book-Length Story

# THE INDIAN HEART OF CARRIE HODGES

by Katy Peake

Carrie was only five years old when Foster Gant first saw her, turning and wheeling with her arms outstretched. Foster knew she wasn't imitating the hawk that was circling high above her head. She was being the hawk. A year passed before Foster saw Carrie again, and this time he gave her a puppy. Tippy, for that was what Carrie called the puppy, became her constant companion.

Foster Gant worked for the State Office of Fish and Game. Each summer he spent a few weeks in the valley checking on the size and movement of the mountain lion population.

Each spring Carrie looked forward to Foster's return. And with each visit her sense of kinship with the animals grew stronger. When Foster was there, Carrie absorbed all he could tell her from his lifetime of observation. He told her of the Indian ways and the magical relations that had existed between the Indians and the animals.

When Carrie was eleven, Foster told her about the animal spirits. He said the Indians believed each person had an animal spirit that would reveal itself when the person was ready. It was not long before Carrie began an earnest search for signs that would reveal her own animal spirit.

The beginning of March brought a week of gentle, sun-filled days. Under cloudless skies the ranch burst forth in a dazzling display of color and new life.

Carrie was overjoyed to have a weekend begin with such a welcome invitation to the outdoors. Sunrise found her dressing herself at the open window of her room. Never, she thought, in all the world had there ever been a green as beautiful as the green of the surrounding hills.

In the permanent pasture below, she could see the horses enjoying the first touch of morning warmth, and among them was Hank, her very own horse.

Carrie ran out to feed Hank. Then she made herself a quick breakfast of dry cereal and milk while she decided how to use this lovely morning. She finally chose to make her first visit of the new year to the river bottom to investigate the changes left behind by the winter floods. She gave Tippy a treat of some leftover bacon,

and they set off together, down through the family orchard and across the permanent pasture.

They stopped there for a while among the sheep.
Carrie had a special interest in the little ewe and her twin
lambs and liked to think of them as her own. The twins
had become very tame and followed her; they nibbled
at her fingers and clothing. Even Tippy came in for a
share of their attention. After Carrie and Tippy rose to
continue on their way, the lambs went along, leaping
and bucking at their heels, until they passed through the
gate to the river.

Drawn by the sound and sight of running water,
Carrie explored along the mile of river that passed
through the ranch. At one point the thick clumps of
cottonwoods and willows gave way to a wide, sandy area
where the brush had been cleared away and tall trees
were spaced out into a kind of natural grove. It was here
the Hodges had set up two long picnic tables. This was
where they held their barbecues and picnics.

Carrie loved the picnic ground and was glad to find
it in good condition, except for a clutter of fallen
branches. She cleaned away the debris and set about
gathering rocks for the barbecue pit, which had to be
built new every spring.

She had collected a good-sized pile when she stopped
to rest. Tippy was over at the river, fishing. He was enthusiastic about fishing and would stand in a shallow
stretch of water, one foot up, waiting the right moment
to make his strike. Then he'd submerge his head under
the water. Every once in a while he would actually catch
a fish. He'd give it a shake and throw it out on the bank
with a quick toss of his head.

Carrie was watching Tippy with amused affection when her eye was caught by a movement a little to her left. It was a skunk shuffling along in her direction with its black-and-white tail in a low arch. Carrie knew that skunks are the least afraid of all wild animals. With their built-in protection they can afford to be. Without being exactly bold, they just don't go to much trouble to avoid encounters.

With an eye on Tippy, Carrie remembered his "skunk christening" at the age of six months. She had had to lock her miserable, half-blind puppy out of her room for a week. After that he had kept his distance and treated all skunks with considerable respect.

The animal was within ten feet of Carrie before it seemed to notice that she was there. She began to think it was strangely unconcerned even for a skunk. When it did see her, instead of turning its backside and lifting its tail, it began to pat its front feet on the ground and move its head from side to side. When Carrie stepped backward, away from the skunk, it darted toward her. It was strange and wrong. She was frightened.

"Tippy!" she called. "Come here, boy." Tippy looked up from his fishing, took a sniff, and whined without moving. "Tippy!" she called again. "Tippy, please come here. Tippy!"

Tippy responded to her urgent call. He came toward her cautiously, making a wide arc around the skunk. At Tippy's approach, the skunk became excited and increased the rhythm of its patting. When Tippy reached Carrie's side, the skunk bared its teeth and made a sudden lunge at her. She jumped back and stumbled over the pile of rocks. Tippy grabbed the skunk by its neck.

The struggle lasted only a moment, but before it was over the skunk had released its odor and had managed to sink its teeth in Tippy's upper lip. The spray had missed its target, but the odor it left was unbearable, sending Carrie and Tippy on a swift and miserable dash for home.

When Carrie told her father, he was immediately worried. "Did you touch that skunk?" he asked. "Did you touch it at all?"

"No, I left it right where Tippy killed it."

"I think we'd better go back down and have a look. You're sure it's dead, Carrie?"

"Yes, I'm sure. Tippy broke its neck. I'm sure of that."

"Come on, then." Gordon Hodges got a shovel and a gunnysack, and they walked back down to the river bottom. Carrie's father lifted the dead skunk with the shovel while Carrie held the sack open. He had her make certain that she held it wide enough to clear the skunk's body while he slipped it in.

As he took the sack from Carrie and tied it shut, he said to her with quiet earnestness, "I'm not just making a fuss for nothing, Carrie. When a wild animal, or any animal for that matter, acts in an unnatural way without any apparent reason, you have to think about rabies. From what you told me about this skunk, it sounds suspicious. Even a mouse will attack if it's rabid. We'll have to take this skunk to Doc Larsen and have him send the brain to the state lab in Sacramento to get it checked."

"Why? Is rabies so terrible? And why does it matter so much if I touched the skunk?"

"Listen, Carrie," her father replied. "I don't want to scare you, but there isn't anything much worse than rabies. It gets to the brain and makes animals crazy; people, too. There isn't any cure for it. Anything that has rabies dies. You can get the disease by being bitten or even from the saliva of a rabid animal—if it gets into a cut or any open place in your skin."

In a sudden panic Carrie remembered the bite on Tippy's lip.

"What about Tippy?" she asked. "What about him?" Tippy whined and rubbed against her leg. She reached down to scratch the soft hollow behind his ear.

"With the shots he's had every two years, Tippy should be all right," Gordon answered, "but we'd better make sure. We'll take him along with the skunk to Doc Larsen's and let him take a look at that bite and maybe find out a few things we ought to know."

He's worried, Carrie thought, and felt a fresh tug of alarm.

"There's one thing I do know, Carrie, baby," Gordon said in a suddenly soft voice, his eyes gravely tender. "We can be mighty grateful to this old dog of yours. The rabies shots they have to give to people when they're bitten are pretty grim. I'm glad you don't have to go through that."

The twenty-minute drive to the animal hospital was a silent one. Gordon seemed lost in thought. Carrie, sitting between her father and Tippy, kept a protecting arm around her dog's neck and tried to fight off the gnawing pain in the pit of her stomach.

When they told Doc Larsen their story, his round and usually cheerful face became serious. He, too, asked Carrie if she was certain she hadn't handled the skunk in any way.

"I'll tell you what," he said. "First thing we'll do is clean that bite out. Now, let's see. I've got Tippy's record . . . mmm . . . Here it is. Rabies shot due July 15, last year." He looked up. "Unless he got it somewhere else, he's about eight months overdue."

"Good grief!" Gordon blurted out. "I was in Arizona that week and never picked up on it when I got back."

In a tense voice that was barely a whisper, Carrie asked, "Does that mean a shot wouldn't do him any good if you gave it to him right away?"

Looking at her drawn face, Doc Larsen put a gentle hand on her shoulder. "Now, Carrie," he said, "don't you go to worrying before you have to. Tippy most

likely still has a good deal of immunity left, and remember, we don't know if we've got a problem here or not. Just to be on the safe side, I'm going to treat your dog as though he's definitely been exposed to rabies. It's a good thing you brought him today. This way we've got time on our side, whatever happens. I'm going to start Tippy on a series of shots that can't do him any harm and will have a good chance of stopping anything before it gets started. That means you'll have to leave him here."

"How long?" Carrie asked miserably. "How long before Tippy can come home?"

Doc Larsen looked over her head to meet Gordon's eyes. "It might take quite a while," he said slowly. "You'll have to be patient."

"I'm afraid I'm pretty rusty on the details, Doc," Gordon said. "Carrie's got to know what to expect."

"Well," Doc Larsen replied, "it may take from about two weeks to fifty days." He didn't add that it might even be several months.

Carrie looked up at her father. "That means Tippy has to stay here all that time, doesn't it?"

"Yes," Gordon replied. "That's what it means."

"He isn't going to understand," Carrie protested. "He'll think he's being punished for something and he won't know why. It isn't fair!" Her eyes filled with tears, and she bit her lip to hold them back.

"We should have the report on the skunk in a week or ten days." Doc Larsen turned to Carrie. "And remember now, if all that ailed that critter was a little unfriendly streak, your dog could go home with more immunity than any dog in California."

Carrie smiled faintly to show Doc Larsen that she appreciated his effort to cheer her up. "Good-bye,

Tippy," she said. "I'll come to get you just as soon as I can."

Somehow Carrie knew it was useless to hope that the skunk's attack had been the act of a normal animal. She could see that little snarling face again with its bloodshot eyes and the saliva dripping from its open mouth. She kept saying to herself over and over again, "You're going to be all right, Tippy. You're going to be all right."

Ten days later when Doc Larsen phoned to say that the report came back—rabies—Carrie took the news quietly but felt the lump of fear inside grow heavier. Forty more days and it's going to be all over. She counted them as they went by.

She had counted to thirty-five when she came home from school and found her mother and father waiting for her in the kitchen.

"Carrie, I have bad news for you," Gordon said. "And there's no way to make it easy."

As she listened with dread to her father's voice, Carrie could feel her mother's eyes on her face. Her heart skipped, and she scarcely heard the dreaded words. "Tippy started to show signs this morning. There was no doubt, Doc said. It was rabies."

Carrie held on to the chair, her face and knuckles suddenly as white as the tablecloth. In a strange, tight voice that seemed to come from somewhere else, she heard herself say, "What are they going to do? Can't they wait to see if he gets better?"

"There isn't any cure for rabies, Carrie. You know that. It's already done. Tippy's gone. There wasn't anything else to do."

A terrifying chill shook Carrie's body. For a moment she lost the power to see or feel. All at once the blood rushed to her head and she let out a cry. "How could you forget his shots? How could you?"

At the sight of her father's strained look she fled from the room.

It was fully dark when she returned from the river bottom, where she had wandered, weeping in grief for Tippy and in regret for having struck out so cruelly at her father. In her room she found a sandwich and a glass of milk, left there by her mother. After one bite Carrie found that she couldn't swallow the sandwich, but the milk went down more easily.

There was the lightest of knocks on her door, and Gordon came into the room. All at once Carrie was in his arms. "Oh, Papa, I'm so sorry! I'm so sorry! I never should have said it to you. I didn't mean it—it just came out of me. I love you so much."

"Carrie, baby, that's all right. I did forget. I'll never in this world be able to tell you how sorry I am, but I really did forget. You've got a right to be angry."

Carrie felt relieved and comforted, but her grief remained, a heavy pain inside.

One day soon after Tippy's death, Carrie found a little rock that was colored just like he had been. The rock was shaped almost like an animal, and she tried carving it until it looked to her like a little dog. She made a buckskin pouch for it and wore it around her neck on a leather string. In one of her Indian books there was a picture of a carved rock something like hers. The book told her only that it was a fetish and that it was supposed to have magic powers. Carrie hoped that Tippy's spirit lived in her rock, and she wore it wherever she went, even to school.

# The Valley of the Moon

The months dragged for Carrie. She longed for the end of school and most of all for Foster's return. Her grief over Tippy's death diminished her usual pleasure at the first signs of the summer season.

Summer in the valley paid little attention to the calendar. It could begin on a different day each year—the day after the last rain had fallen and the long dry spell had begun. This day could occur anytime between the middle of March and the first week in May.

This year there had been no rain since the third week of March, and a long, hard frost had followed that. Feed was in short supply, and for the first time Carrie could remember, the upper springs had gone dry before June.

The wild animals were driven to low ground near the houses to forage for food. They prowled about in the late morning long after their usual hunting hours. Raccoons and foxes became bold about stealing from the fruit trees in the orchard. The grapevine by the tank house was stripped bare before Carrie had tasted a single grape. The pasture grass passed quickly from green through golden brown and was dull gray by the time Foster showed up toward the end of July.

At first his presence brought the loss of Tippy back to Carrie with terrible sharpness. "It's not too often you find a dog like that owl-headed friend of yours," Foster told her. "He was one of the good ones." Carrie could find no words to explain that part of her love for Tippy was due to the fact that Foster had brought him to her. She would always be grateful to have had him.

One morning following Foster's arrival, Carrie rode with him to the high cliff at the far end of the ranch. There were several wind caves located about halfway up the cliff, which was broken by a series of narrow ledges. Earlier in the year Carrie had made the difficult climb to the caves and explored them. They were disappointingly shallow. Their look of mystery was misleading. They held no secrets, as she had hoped, and it was a long way back down to safe ground.

Carrie asked Foster if he had ever been up there, and he said, "Yes. They aren't much, are they?"

"I was hoping I'd find some Indian paintings."

"Indians would never use a place like that. Too open, and the sandstone's too soft." Foster reached over and touched the hawk feathers Carrie had tied in Hank's mane. "You're pretty serious about this Indian stuff, aren't you?"

Carrie found it impossible, even then, to tell Foster about the search for her own animal spirit and its secret importance to her.

Foster seemed to sense something behind Carrie's silence. In his high, bird-thin voice he said, "You know, I have a mind to show you something."

He led off on Belle, and Carrie followed on Hank. They crossed a shallow canyon, then climbed up to a small meadow where there was a spring-fed trough and one big sycamore tree. It was the highest watering place on the ranch. From this spot they could look clear on down to the ranch yard. Beyond it they could see the floor of the valley, where the river flowed westward toward the sea.

Carrie knew the meadow well. It was one of her best and most frequently used lookout posts. To the east, from the edge of the meadow on up to the skyline, one could see only brush.

Foster dismounted, and Carrie followed suit. "This might take us a little while," he said, "but it's early yet. I think we'll make it all right."

Carrie followed his example as he tied Belle's lead rope to a branch of the sycamore and walked over to where the brush began. It was a thick patch of sage and greasewood, heavily leafed almost down to the ground.

"Didn't come prepared, but this will help a little." He showed Carrie a brush knife. "Watch your eyes," he warned. And dropping down to his hands and knees, he began to crawl into the thicket.

Carrie followed as closely as she could. Foster had a way in that brush. He crawled through places that seemed impossible as easy as a weasel slipping down a hole. Carrie had a hard time keeping up. Before they

had gone twenty feet, she had lost a hank of hair and had a long, bleeding scratch right through her shirt sleeve. Foster would wait for her and let her catch her breath a little. Then without a word he'd start into an opening she hadn't even seen. Every once in a while they would come across a widened place where wild hogs had bedded down. There the ground would be smooth, and the going would be easy.

It was almost dark under the heavy covering. Carrie couldn't understand how Foster kept his sense of direction. Hers had gone almost immediately.

Once they heard the buzz of a rattlesnake. "More'n twenty feet away and bound to go somewhere else," Foster reassured her. That's the only thing he said the entire time they crawled. It took almost two hours before they saw an edge of light and came out on the other side.

They emerged onto a narrow, grassy ledge. From her hands and knees Carrie couldn't see past the rim where it dropped off. Her legs were cramped and sore, and both knees were raw from crawling. Her hair was full of twigs, and she could see four wood ticks on her arms and shirt front. Foster looked as good as new. He gave himself a little shake and stood up.

Carrie spit out a twig and brushed her head as well as she could. She paid special attention to the back of her neck and the inside of her shirt collar. If she had ticks on the front of her, she could well imagine what the rest of her was like.

All that was forgotten when Carrie went to stand at the rim of the ledge beside Foster. Her heart pounded as she looked down on a sight she could never have

imagined. Thirty feet below was a fairly large clearing. All around the sides of the clearing stood huge, fantastic sandstone rocks. They had been carved by the wind into twisting, intermingling shapes of animals. In the center of the clearing were other rocks, low, dark, and moss covered. They sprawled about like half-submerged prehistoric monsters.

Foster touched Carrie's arm and started down the steep incline. If he spoke to her, she didn't remember. Together they explored the magic landscape.

There was one lone tree, an ancient wide-branched giant oak. How an acorn came to be planted there so long ago was one of the valley's secrets.

Leaning up against the thick trunk of the old tree, Foster began to talk.

"One time before, I saw a place like this," he said. "And that was in the Zuñi Indian country in Arizona. An old Zuñi hunter told me that it held a very sacred place in their history about the beginning of the world."

Then in his strange, quiet voice that seemed like part of a dream, Foster told Carrie a legend. "When the earth was still soft, there were monsters and hunting animals that came up out of the mud and devoured people. The children of the Sun Father saw that in order to protect the people the earth had to be hardened. They did that with bolts of lightning, and the surface of the earth got dried out. Then the beasts of prey were free to walk around on the hard ground, and the people continued to be devoured. The Sun Father's children began to strike individual animals with lightning, and those animals were turned to stone. The heart of each animal remained alive within the stone, and the stone held the spirit and magic powers of the real live animal.

"When the Zuñi found small rocks that resembled animals, they considered them to be the animals that had been struck and shriveled by lightning. Those roughly shaped rocks were the Zuñi's first fetishes. The rocks were carved and polished by the Indians, who believed that carrying them helped the hunter find game.

"The fetish established a special connection between the spirit of the hunter and the spirit of the animal being hunted. The fetish had the further power of protecting the hunter from harm.

"Sometimes when the lightning struck, the animals would not be shriveled but would remain life-sized and in groups, just as they had been at the moment when they were turned to stone."

Foster continued, still speaking in the same quiet voice. "First time I was here was years ago, long before I talked with that old Indian. Just seemed to me I'd stumbled into another world, and I named this place the Valley of the Moon. Just kind of stuck."

Carrie sat there for a while beside Foster with her throat choked up and her head spinning. Then she took out her Tippy rock and handed it to him. He looked at it for a long time and rubbed it with his hand. "Carrie Hodges," he said, "I do believe you have an Indian heart." Carrie felt a wild surge of joy that was like a bright light all around her. It was a sign, a true sign. There could be no doubt about it.

The homeward journey was a sleepwalker's dream to Carrie. The spell cast by the Valley of the Moon held her just as if she were still there.

In this vague and dreamlike state Carrie heard Foster explain to her worried parents the reason for their lateness. Just what he told them about the Valley of the Moon remained unclear to her. Foster's explanation was too brief for him to have said a great deal. The secret of the valley would remain hers and Foster's.

The following day Foster said his farewells. Carrie cried a little when he loaded Belle in the trailer and pulled out of the yard.

After he was gone, the meaning of the shared adventure was Carrie's to deal with alone. Thoughts of returning to the valley filled her waking and sleeping hours. She was more determined than ever to find her own animal spirit. But her quest must remain a secret. To reveal it might spoil the magic.

One night at dinner Gordon Hodges took hold of his daughter's hand. "See here, Carrie!" he scolded. "Stop daydreaming about that place long enough to eat. Else some little old bird will pick you right up and drop you in there like a thistle seed."

"I wouldn't care if it did!" she blurted out.

Gordon gave her one of his see-right-through-you looks. Slowly, Carrie met his eyes. He smiled a tiny smile and let her keep her secret, whole and unharmed.

Sometimes, as the days went by, Carrie returned to the sycamore meadow and scanned the brushy hills for

some indication of her enchanted valley. She prowled the wall of greasewood and sage looking for a path to open, although she knew there would be none.

Once she crawled a hundred yards or more into the thicket, and became confused in the directionless gloom. She fought her way back out with a panicky heart.

Her scratched and tattered state gave her away, and her father asked her to give him her word that she wouldn't try it again. Next spring, he promised, he would somehow find the time to cut a trail into the valley.

Spring seemed forever away, but Carrie had a plan. She would go prepared with her own magic when she returned to the Valley of the Moon.

During the little time that was left of summer, Carrie searched for animal-shaped rocks that would become her fetishes. She gathered, selected, compared, and discarded. Soon she had a satisfying collection, which she kept in a wooden box under her bed. In the evenings she got them out and worked at shaping and smoothing them with pieces of flint.

The fetishes took form gradually, with a few failures along the way. Some of the rocks proved too difficult to carve. Others broke in the making. They were crude, even cruder than the pictures in the book she used as a guide, but as she worked they became lifelike to her.

She began to carry them with her whenever she went out. Each time she saw a matching animal, she felt certain of the magic powers of her fetishes.

Fox, bobcat, raccoon, mountain lion, and deer—Carrie finished all her main animals, with the exception of the coyote. She wanted a very special rock for that, and she knew that sooner or later she would find it.

# A Sign of the Coyote

It was on a weekend in early October that Carrie finally found her coyote stone. She found it in a sandy gully not too far above the ranch yard. It was a small yellowish-brown piece of rock that gave forth a rich glow when she rubbed it with her hand.

Almost next to it was a partially buried horse's skull, which must have been there for many years before it was exposed. Fine grit and sand had polished the bone to the look and feel of old ivory. Carrie dug up one half of the lower jawbone alongside the skull, but the other half wasn't to be found.

It was a beautiful find in itself and seemed to Carrie to be some kind of omen. She was determined to locate the rest of the jawbone, so she drove an upright stick into the ground to mark the spot. At the same time, she noted a moss-covered valley oak on the bank above.

When Carrie went back to continue her search the following weekend, she saw a coyote that she could always identify. It was a young female that she had seen for the first time as a pup. What set this coyote apart was the odd, low set of her ears, which never stood fully upright. Also, there was the darkness of her coat that had more distinctly marked shadings than are usual. Carrie had seen her off and on for more than a year. She had even been lucky enough to track her to the den where the coyote had her own first litter.

When Carrie spotted her, the lop-eared female was trotting along a cow path with a dead ground squirrel in her mouth. The path she was following was taking her away from where Carrie knew her den to be. Instead, it was leading her toward the canyon where Carrie was headed in search of the missing jawbone.

Carrie was out in the open, but the coyote took no heed as she trotted along in her businesslike way. Suddenly, she disappeared behind a clump of greasewood.

As Carrie made her way down the steep incline, she noticed a fresh scar high up on the trunk of the valley oak. A branch had snapped off and fallen since her last visit. The branch, which was long and thick, now lay across the gully, forming a low bridge.

As she got closer, Carrie could smell the odor of dead animal. Then, sticking out from under the oak branch, she discovered the carcasses of three half-grown coyote cubs. They had been crushed together by the weight of the fallen branch. Right above them, wedged in a fork of the branch, was the missing piece of jawbone. It probably had been put there by some hunter a long time ago. It was bleached white and pitted by age and exposure.

The cubs had been dead for several days. Their bodies were badly decayed and the carcasses torn apart. At least, Carrie hoped, they must have died at once.

Then Carrie remembered the coyote she had seen carrying the squirrel and apparently headed this way. Coyotes are practical animals, and this one wouldn't be spending useless time trying to feed dead cubs. If they were hers, there had to be a living cub close by.

She looked around and found it lying, broken and helpless, where the mother had dragged it to cover. Its wild eyes, full of fear and pain, fixed on her. Even in that condition, it drew its lips back and snarled. Carrie looked up to meet the eyes of its mother on the bank above. The

coyote dropped the squirrel and stared back without a trace of fear. Feeling a sick pain at the pit of her stomach, Carrie pulled the jawbone from the branch. With one hard blow she killed the cub.

She looked up to somehow seek forgiveness from the mother, but the coyote was gone. Carrie made a little grave and buried the cub. She put a mound of rocks on top as a mark of respect.

The incident wouldn't leave Carrie, and for a long time she found herself turning it over in her mind. Had the spirit of her coyote stone brought her there and given her the weapon to perform that awful act of mercy?

The strangest part of it was that after the incident Carrie began to see the lop-eared coyote quite frequently. Once she caught a brief glimpse of the coyote traveling a course not far from her own — but at a barely cautious distance.

One afternoon Carrie was watching a pair of red-shouldered hawks attack a California red-tailed hawk that was attempting to move into their territory. The smaller hawks circled about, striking at the redtail until it began to show signs of defeat.

The fight was just about over when Carrie had the strange feeling of being watched. She looked around and spotted, just over the edge of the hill, the dark back and sides of the coyote. The lop-eared female knew at once that Carrie had seen her. But instead of playing her usual dodging game, the coyote showed herself in full view. She came within twenty yards of Carrie and sat down, letting her tongue loll out.

They were so close to the ranch yard that Carrie
heard her mother calling her for dinner. Carrie stood up,
careful to make her motions smooth. The coyote stood
up, too, but made no move to run. She watched as Carrie
turned for home. She wagged her tail and followed at a
distance half-way down the hill, in plain view the whole
time.

After that, the coyote started showing up just about
every time Carrie went out in the hills by herself. She
let Carrie watch her, but she never came closer than that
first distance she had established. Carrie never tried to
tame her by offering her food or approaching her in any

way. The coyote often wagged her tail or jumped in the air and spun around when she first caught sight of Carrie.

Occasionally, from her bedroom window, Carrie saw the coyote, cutting through the orchard on her way to the river bottom. Whenever she was with her mate, she would give no sign that she had ever seen Carrie before. Her behavior gave Carrie a deep and secret excitement. Was this, too, some kind of an omen? She could almost feel the power of her coyote fetish when she held it in her hand.

November came without a cloud in the sky. The people of the valley began to wear the tense and worried look of disaster. There seemed to be no end to the drought.

Gordon and Elinore Hodges were on edge with each other and slow to smile. Sometimes her parents didn't seem to hear what Carrie said, and for the first time in her life she began to feel lonely.

Just before Thanksgiving Uncle Ed came to spend his vacation with the Hodges. Uncle Ed was Gordon Hodges' brother. He was a lawyer and unlike Carrie's father in every way, except that he was almost as tall. The skin on his hands was pale and smooth. His dark hair was slicked back.

Uncle Ed wore his country clothes when he came to visit. They were always the same—gaudy wool jacket, dark-green pants, and laced-up hiking boots that squeaked when he walked. It always took a few days for the smell of mothballs to wear off his clothes.

Uncle Ed said that his vacation on the ranch was the high point of his year. From the time Carrie was born, he had brought her presents. This year he brought Carrie a compass to keep her from losing her way. She smiled as she tucked it away in her drawer.

Uncle Ed was the clumsiest-moving man Carrie had ever seen. He claimed to love the country and all it held, but he would never stop talking long enough to let the country happen around him.

Carrie's parents loved having Uncle Ed come. Gordon and his brother would remember incidents from their childhood and sit up laughing and talking long after Carrie and her mother had gone to bed. Gordon Hodges allowed himself to take things easy during Uncle Ed's visits. One sign of this was what Gordon jokingly referred to as "going for our morning canter." This was a horseback ride undertaken by the entire Hodges family, solely for pleasure.

Uncle Ed on a horse would have been more of a bother than a help around the ranch. But he did love to ride! And this outing provided him with the only possible excuse for wearing his gaudy jacket and western boots. He rode happily, if carelessly, and drowned out the birds with his own western songs.

As they started out that year for their "morning canter," Uncle Ed was mounted on an old retired horse called Catcher. Carrie's father had told her once that his entire name was Fool Catcher. He had been named that because, no matter what fool thing was done on him, old Catcher would stay under his rider. On this occasion Uncle Ed managed to break Catcher's record. It happened as the group crossed a little gully that rose in a steep bank on the far side. Catcher was humped for the climb, and Uncle Ed was letting him go about it any way he saw fit. Uncle Ed sat turned around in the saddle, the bridle reins dangling, as he talked to Carrie behind him.

Carrie saw the saddle start to slip back and the cinch hanging loose under Catcher's belly. She tried to warn Uncle Ed about the cinch, but there was no way he could be interrupted. It was fascinating to watch Uncle Ed, saddle and all, slipping in slow motion right off the hind end of that horse. As Catcher gave a lunge, Uncle Ed landed in the dust, still sitting in the saddle. He had a look of stunned astonishment on his face. Everyone laughed so hard they cried. Carrie couldn't think of an animal spirit for Uncle Ed, but as a natural clown, a raccoon seemed the closest fit.

Uncle Ed's arrival hadn't brought rain, but it had helped to break the gloomy mood that hovered over the ranch. One day, Gordon decided to go to Utah to take a look at some yearling steers. Uncle Ed would go along for company.

Whenever Gordon went away for more than a day, he asked Mr. Corbellini to come stay in the bunkhouse. Mr. Corbellini, who lived with his son and daughter-in-law about a mile down the road, could help look after things around the ranch.

Carrie liked Mr. Corbellini. He knew how to make and mend things. Once he brought Carrie a curved sack needle when she was having trouble pushing a straight one through the leather of the moccasins she was making. He often told her about growing up in the Italian village where he was born. Carrie thought Mr. Corbellini's animal spirit would be a badger.

This year it turned out that Mr. Corbellini was sick with the flu and couldn't come. The only person that Gordon could find to help out while he was gone was Leo McCready.

"I know you don't like Leo," he told Carrie and Elinore. "I don't much care for him myself, but he'll know what to do. I told him there wasn't to be any shooting on this place while I'm away. It's just going to be for a week, and maybe less if I can make it."

From the time she had first seen Leo McCready, Carrie had felt uncomfortable in his presence. He had a lot of free time on his hands and often showed up for cattle branding whether he was invited or not. Leo was always rough with the animals, and Carrie thought he seemed to take real pleasure in hurting them.

Leo did more talking than anyone else at the brandings, and Carrie hated the stories he told. They were mostly about trapping and shooting wild animals, or varmints, as he called them.

Carrie decided that if Leo had an animal spirit it would be a wolverine, a destructive animal that kills for pleasure beyond its own need for food. Indians considered the wolverine to be an evil spirit in itself. To Carrie that seemed to fit Leo McCready in every way.

Carrie dreaded Leo McCready's presence on the ranch, but she would just have to bear it for a week. She reminded herself that there was school to go to, homework to do, and finishing touches to put on her fetishes.

When Gordon and Uncle Ed were gone, and Leo was settled in the bunkhouse, Carrie found she could manage to avoid the sight and sound of him almost completely, except at mealtimes. Then she and her mother had to put up with his long, windy stories and his bad manners.

Two days after the men had left, the weather turned sharply cold. There was frost every night, and coyotes began to sing in the fullness of a pale and wintry moon.

# Impending Trouble

It was on the third morning that Leo found a dead lamb in the permanent pasture. His mean eyes seemed to gloat as he said to Carrie, "I guess there's one coyote don't fall under your dad's protection."

Early the following day before it was light, Carrie heard the crack of two shots and was filled with hatred and fear.

"Missed the old varmint," Leo grunted when Carrie ran out to meet his pickup as it came up the driveway. "But I got a good look at her, and I'll tell you one thing, this wasn't no ordinary coyote. I seen some like her before, and they mean trouble. They're half dog, that's what they are. They make the worst kind of killers, and there's no way of telling how many like 'em you got out there."

Carrie felt a chill of fear and a sense of impending trouble. She began to count the minutes until her father returned and the ranch would be free of Leo's menacing presence.

The day of the travelers' homecoming brought Carrie three reasons for rejoicing: Leo, at long last, departed; her father was there to put things right again; and it rained. Four inches fell during that first storm, which Gordon foresaw as the beginning of a long, wet winter. The gloom cast by the dry spell vanished from the ranch as preparations for the rainy season got under way.

Carrie was tempted to confide her feelings about Leo to her father, but, somehow, Leo seemed less menacing now that Gordon was home. She did tell her father about the sheep-killing incident, but her concern for the lop-eared coyote she kept to herself.

It rained off and on through December and January. There was an early lambing season, and most of the ewes had lambed out by the middle of February. Then, during a spell of clear, warm weather, the sheep were moved to the permanent pasture. Within a week's time, the remains of three killings were found.

One afternoon when Carrie got home from school, Leo's pickup was in the yard, and lying in the back of it was the body of the lop-eared coyote. The full look that life had given her was completely gone. Carrie's hatred was so great she could hardly control herself.

Leo met Carrie's eyes with a pleased smirk. "Half dog just like I said."

Leo did his evil work well. News that a sheep-killing, half-dog coyote had been shot on the Hodges' place was all around the valley in a day's time. The talk grew into a rash of stories about packs of wild half-dogs that had no fear. They would kill livestock of any kind right in broad daylight. There were reports of other livestock losses. Word spread that a tainted strain threatened the entire valley and that the half-dogs would teach the pure-bred coyotes to invade the farmyards and pastures. Fear grew into panic as the idea took over the minds of the people.

Once the coyotes had become tainted, the ranchers said, there was only one thing to do. That was to hunt down and kill every last living coyote in the valley.

Talk of the coming hunt took place everywhere. Professional hunters were called in from places as far away as Texas. The hunt was set for the middle of March, when the coyotes would begin to whelp and could be killed in their dens.

Carrie could not hide her distress. Her parents watched her with pity and gave what comfort they could. Gordon said this sort of panic generally died down before anything came of it. Elinore said she hoped that Leo McCready would get caught in one of his own traps. She never wanted to set eyes on him again.

The days and nights were nearly unbearable for Carrie. She was tormented by the thought that in some way she was responsible for what was happening. Her search had angered the spirits. The signs along the way had been meant to stop her from continuing, but she had not heeded their warnings. First there had been Tippy's death, then the coyote cubs, and finally their lop-eared mother. The horse's skull had been a sign, too.

Carrie's torment led her to wonder if there was any way the lives of the coyotes could be spared.

Lying sleepless in her bed one night, she saw clearly what she had to do. She had to go to the Valley of the Moon and ask for help.

Carrie dressed quickly and warmly and made her preparations. She unrolled her sleeping bag and put in her hunting knife and a box of matches. Then she filled the water gourd she had been seasoning since last summer and made certain the wooden plug she had carved fit it tightly. She slipped into the kitchen and made a little bundle of bread, cheese, and dried fruit. Those things went into the bag, along with the knife and matches. Then she rolled the bag and tied it into a small bundle.

She stood thinking for a moment about what else she might need, and then put a flashlight and the compass Uncle Ed had given her in her pocket. She slipped her arms through the backpack loops she had made for the bag. The coyote fetish was already in the pouch that hung around her neck. She was ready.

As Carrie slipped out of the house and crossed the yard, a full moon marked the night as half gone. It would take three good hours of walking to reach the meadow. How long it would take to find her way through the brush she couldn't guess. And after that? Carrie was suddenly afraid that time would run out, that her journey would be discovered, and that she would never accomplish her purpose. Then, as though the words were being spoken aloud, she recalled something her father had said a long time ago: *I'll bet Old Blue could carry you to the moon and back.* That had been a sign, too. She recognized it now.

Blue stood at the gate of his pen as though waiting for her, and for the first time in her life Carrie climbed on the back of her father's horse. Riding him was like floating through the moonlit landscape. Blue's long strides ate up the hills, and Carrie's own spirit lifted as she was carried along on the first part of her journey.

There in the meadow Carrie tied Blue to the sycamore tree. She thanked him and kissed his nose and asked him to be patient. Then she began the long crawl through the thicket that sprawled dark and leaden between the meadow and the Valley of the Moon.

Almost immediately Carrie was in darkness. Her flashlight penetrated only a foot or so ahead. Branches and thorns clawed at her face and clothes. The bulk of the sleeping bag made her progress even more difficult than it had been when she had come with Foster. She heard animal sounds from time to time and was terrified as she had never been before. The chill of terror and the winter night numbed her body and brought cramps to her legs.

Carrie wept with fear and made no attempt to stop the tears, but not once did she think of going back. It was only Uncle Ed's compass that made it possible for her to keep crawling toward the east. Carrie laughed out loud when she realized that it, too, had been a sign. Because it came from dear, funny Uncle Ed, she hadn't given it a thought, not even when she had stuck it in her pocket.

Carrie had lost all sense of time. Only when she saw the moon riding low in the western sky as she crawled the last few feet did she realize that the night was far along and she must hurry. Then she was out of the brush and looking down into the Valley of the Moon.

Even memory and longing had not prepared her for this landscape in full moonlight. The rocks rose up from the floor of the valley, seeming to draw far more than their share of light from the moon. In sharp contrast, the surrounding brush was veiled in darkness.

Were the rocks warning her of impending danger? Was she to go no farther? She hesitated for a moment, then took a step forward. She would not turn back.

As she descended into the valley, she sought the location of the old oak. In the midst of all this magic strangeness it seemed a familiar friend. She sought comfort from its thick trunk and low-spread branches. It was here that she planned to make her camp.

# A Different World

Under the tree Carrie smoothed a piece of ground and spread out her sleeping bag. Then she dug a shallow pit and put an edging of small rocks around the top. From the bits and pieces of dried and broken oak branches that lay scattered about, she found enough wood to build a campfire. There was enough left over to make a pile of wood for later on. She set aside her little bundle of bread, dried fruit, and cheese. That was for morning. Tonight Carrie would fast. The water gourd she kept by her side.

Carrie took out the coyote fetish from the buckskin pouch that hung inside her shirt. She rubbed the dust away until it showed its soft polish of rich, golden brown. For, whatever might result, this was the most beautiful fetish she had made, a symbol of her kinship with the coyote. She placed it near the edge of the fire in a standing position, so that the light would fall on it.

"Carrie Hodges," she said to herself, "if you really have an Indian heart, please let it work now. Let the coyote spirits listen to it speak."

This was the moment of testing—testing what she believed and wanted to believe. Carrie thought long and hard about how to begin. Finally she started by speaking out loud.

"Friend Coyotes," she began earnestly. "If you can hear me, listen to me, please." Her words and voice sounded childish and futile. How could such a feeble summoning cause the coyotes to sense her presence and her purpose?

In the many times Carrie had been seen by the animals, she had felt them lose a certain degree of shyness and caution when she was around. They had become used to her as a quiet observer of their lives and ways. Yet there had been no clear sign that her fetishes had caused her to be recognized as a friendly spirit. Only with the lop-eared coyote had it been different, and she was dead, perhaps by Carrie's doing.

Maybe there had been no signs, after all, and she was just a twelve-year-old girl playing at Indian magic. Carrie could not bear that to be true. She had broken her sacred promise to her father in order to come into the forbidden valley.

She sat with her arms locked around her knees, staring into the fire. A small bird called out, alarmed in the night.

Then a coyote barked sharply from a long way off. Carrie listened hard, but the sound was not repeated. She put another stick on the fire and thought about getting into her sleeping bag to keep warm. But the pile of wood was going too fast, and she decided first to gather more for the rest of the night.

The coyote barked again. This time the sound was much closer and more prolonged. The coyote began with a series of sharp barks, then broke into a cascade of rising and falling notes. A new voice joined in, then another, and yet another, each weaving in and out until the notes grew more and more prolonged. They reached a wild, piercing volume that stabbed Carrie through with loving despair. Then came a last solo voice, which diminished gradually and was gone.

How could anyone who had ever heard that sound in the night not want to hear it again?

The little stone coyote had fallen over on its side. Carrie set it straight again and took a long drink from the gourd. Then she slipped into her sleeping bag, and with her hands clasped beneath her head, looked up at the stars. The good smells of the earth and decaying leaves so close to her face brought her comfort. She looked again at the rocks and waited for some sign that the call of the coyotes had been an answer to her summons.

Carrie was feeling a sharp pang of hunger and a strange dizziness in her head, when, beyond the reach of the fire's light, she caught a sudden glimpse of glowing eyes. She stared intently while the unknown watcher remained silent and unmoving. Then the eyes disappeared and in a moment became visible again. A large male coyote stepped out from the shadow of a rock. Lean and low slung, he stood with his head cocked to one side in the manner of a curious dog. Then very slowly and stiff-legged he walked to within a few feet of the fire. He came to a halt and looked directly into Carrie's eyes, then sat down and curled his tail around himself until the tip rested neatly between his forelegs.

Carrie stared back in unbelieving excitement. Another pair of eyes glowed briefly from the shadows, and a female coyote, big with cubs, stepped timidly forward into the light. On dainty feet she approached the male, at the same time watching Carrie with anxious yellow eyes. She stood beside the male, leaning against his shoulder until he nudged her ear with his nose. Then she, too, sat down and curled her tail about herself. Then another coyote and still another came and sat, four full-grown coyotes sitting side by side.

Carrie's heart pounded and her head swam. She had never dreamed of anything so beautiful and so strange. She was completely without fear, filled with awe and the

stirrings of a wild, wonderful hope. Everything seemed to come to a stop while she and the coyotes looked at each other. Even the crickets were still.

Carrie could not tell how long the silence lasted. She remained quiet, fearing that any movement from her would make the visitors run away or simply vanish.

It was the first big male who broke the spell. Carrie was beyond surprise when he began to speak in a clear musical voice.

"Young Friend," he said, "we see that you are not afraid, and that is good." He paused as if to wait for Carrie to respond, but she had lost the power of speech.

"We have come," the coyote continued, "because the night wind was sent forth by the spirits of this sacred place to bring us word that you wished to tell us something of grave importance. The night wind has touched our tongues and blown in our ears so that we speak a common language—for this night only. We have come, therefore, to your fire and to the symbol of kinship you have made of stone. Like the people of ancient times, you come and go in our hills in a spirit of friendship with the wild animals."

In the face of Carrie's continued silence he went on in an encouraging tone. "It is seldom given to humans and animals that they may speak together. It has never happened in our time, or in the time of our parents or grandparents or for many generations before that. The spirits of the rocks are not easily fooled, and I do not think the wind has touched our tongues and blown in our ears for nothing. We have accepted this gift of language, and we have come to speak with you and to hear what you have to tell us."

When the old coyote had finished, Carrie sat upright.

"Yes," she said urgently. "Yes, I do have something to tell you, and it's terribly, terribly important. Here, let me get out of this thing." As Carrie struggled to free herself from the sleeping bag, the coyotes regarded her efforts with amusement. When Carrie was fully out, she could feel the bitter chill of the night air right through her fleece-lined jacket.

She felt shy, and was uncertain how to respond to the coyote's remarks. Her voice cracked, she stumbled over the words, and her face grew red with effort. "I am honored, Wild Friends," she said, "that you have come and that you call me Friend. I have called to you in my thoughts and from my troubled Indian heart. I am well rewarded."

She had begun to feel more comfortable. "And I thank the spirits and the night wind for their good help. What I have come to tell you is that you are in terrible danger, all of you."

As she was speaking, Carrie became aware that other shadowy forms had emerged from behind other rocks. More coyotes and still more were joining the original four. She did not count them but realized that there must be at least twenty coyotes, most of them fully grown. A few were half-grown cubs that stayed in the background and scuffled among themselves. They were just about the same size, Carrie thought, as the four little ones that had died so miserably in the gully. She shivered and was suddenly struck bone cold. "Do you mind," she asked in a polite tone, "if I put more wood on the fire?"

"Not at all," replied the old coyote. "It feels good." He stretched his head back and yawned, rolling his pink tongue far back in his throat and closing his eyes in pleasure.

Carrie put several more sticks of wood on the glowing embers. Then she leaned forward and blew until the wood caught fire and blazed up brightly. When she looked up again, she could feel the power of those many watching eyes. She caught her breath in fresh amazement when she saw that the group had been joined by three bobcats, five foxes, a pair of weasels, and, most incredible of all, a mountain lion.

Seeing Carrie's astonishment, the old coyote said, "Yes, Friend, we have asked all the hunting animals to join us." He made a sweeping gesture with his head, and for the first time Carrie noticed several owls perched at the end of a low-hanging branch of the oak. "They were reluctant to come because you did not summon them. But I am very glad to see that they are here."

The newly arrived animals seated themselves among the coyotes. Only the lion seemed nervous and remained prowling restlessly at the outer edge of the gathering. At last he too sat down, leaving his long tail extended behind him, flicking the tip of it now and then.

Carrie felt that it was her turn to say something. "Greetings to you, Friends of the Coyotes. I do not know that what I have to say will concern you. But I am honored by your presence."

The newcomers did not respond to her greeting, so, after a brief pause, Carrie slipped back into her everyday form of speech to tell them the reasons for her coming. "As I have told the coyotes, they are in great danger. The danger is this: All the ranchers have gotten together to plan the biggest coyote hunt that has ever been held.

They are talking about getting rid of coyotes for good and for all. They say the coyotes are tainted by evil blood from outside their own kind. Because of that, they say, the coyotes will kill and kill until none of the ranch animals will be safe. They are afraid for their livestock and have decided that the coyotes must be killed and the country rid of every last one of them."

"We have been hunted before," said a young female, speaking up in a high, fluty voice. "Shot at, trapped, hounded, and poisoned, but we're still here. Coyotes have always been here."

Surprised to hear a new voice, Carrie looked at the speaker and answered her. "But this is different. I have to make you understand how different. They are bringing in hunters from outside, and dogs, too. Not just the ranch dogs from around here. They're bringing in dogs that are trained to hunt coyotes, hounds to track you down, to dig out your dens, and kill your cubs. They mean what they say, and you just have to believe me that they can do it." Her voice broke, and she couldn't go on.

The animals sat quietly in the silence that followed. Only the weasels squeaked to each other. A whippoorwill called in the distance, and the crickets started up again. There was an uneasy rustling among the animals.

At last the old coyote broke the silence. "This is truly serious. Nothing quite like this has ever occurred before. It is good, indeed, that you have called us.

"We shall have to make a plan," he announced with determination. "We must not be driven from our homes. We must talk this over."

He turned from the fire, and immediately the rest of the animals began to break up into small groups, moving about and mingling with one another. There was little sound as they spoke among themselves in the language of the animals. The owls came down from their perch, and it was strange to see the weasels, bobcats, foxes, and particularly the owls moving freely about in the midst of all the coyotes. The lion alone kept his place, and from time to time the other animals went to consult with him.

Carrie sat there and watched it all, feeling strange and left out. She wished with all her heart to be part of their planning, to share their danger, and to fight with them in defeating the ranchers. She picked up her fetish and held it close to her chest. Again she began to feel dizzy and light-headed, and there was a cramping pain in the pit of her stomach. The scene before her swam. The animals blurred together. Carrie shut her eyes, half expecting that when she opened them again she would be alone with just the rocks of the Valley of the Moon for company.

But all the animals were still there and had gone quietly back to their original positions. As the elderly coyote stepped forward once more, he carried a piece of bark in his mouth, which he placed on the ground in front of him. "We have consulted with one another," he said. "And we are all in agreement as to what we must do. People are sometimes very foolish in the way they try to solve their problems. We are going to take advantage of this foolishness and teach them a lesson. At the same time we will establish our right to live here in peace forever." He spoke slowly and with commanding sternness.

"It is obvious," he went on, "that all the coyotes in the whole world could not join together and fight the ranchers in the manner in which they have chosen to fight us. We do not seek to do anything that is so against our nature and so futile. Nevertheless, we have some natural weapons of our own that will surprise the ranchers. We have voted to take you into our confidence. We respect your courage. We want you to be aware of our plan and to observe the progress of our success. This, then, is our plan:

"We will not run away from our homeland in fear, not even for a day. We will remain, but from this moment forward, we will stop hunting. The other hunting animals have agreed to cooperate with us, and there will be no hunting at all anywhere in the valley." He finished on a tone of angry pride and looked to Carrie for her answer.

"But I don't see," she blurted out, "how that can possibly help. It just means that you will starve yourselves to death instead of being killed by guns and dogs."

"My Young Friend, don't underestimate the wisdom of our idea. If all goes well, and you may be assured it will, our troubles will be over long before the great hunt is due to begin. We will be hungry—yes, we will be that. And it will be a terrible sacrifice for our mates, who are getting close to whelping. In cases of extreme hardship we will permit a few individuals to hunt, but that will be a rare thing.

"You have no idea what will happen if all the hunting animals in this valley stop eating even for a week. We are determined to continue until our purpose is accomplished, no matter how much we must sacrifice. The owls have agreed to talk to the hawks, and the weasels, foxes, and bobcats to the others of their own kind. The foxes have decided that they can make out very well on fruit from the orchards, wild berries, and grasshoppers.

The bobcats are not enthusiastic, but they are going to go along with us. They get shot at and trapped much the way we do. Only the weasels say that they are not certain they can keep the agreement. Well, it's probably too much to expect of weasels," the coyote said with marked distaste. "But then, they did come, and they said they would try. The lion said he thought it was a fine idea, but, as he is single and getting lonely, he has decided to move to the high country and look for companionship.

"You want to know, my Friend and Sister, why this is going to work? Inside a week the ranchers are going to begin to see more rabbits, mice, ground squirrels, gophers, and moles than they have ever seen or heard of in their lives. You have no idea how fast those little fellows multiply when left to their own devices. At first the ranchers may not think too much about it. But in a very little while their hay is going to show damage. Their vegetable gardens will be ruined. The gophers and moles will destroy their lawns and flowers. There will be more burrows than grass where they irrigate, and the alfalfa patch will leak like a sieve. The deer will become fearless, and what the gophers don't ruin of the alfalfa, the deer will.

"Mark my words, the plan will be a success far beyond anything you can imagine. It won't be long before the ranchers will be talking about bringing in coyotes from somewhere else to put things back in order again."

As the old coyote spoke, Carrie became more and more convinced of the truth that lay behind his words. The plan was more daring than she could ever have imagined.

"It's wonderful," she said. "Just plain amazing wonderful." And she was overcome with the realization that only she alone, Carrie Hodges, would know what was going to happen.

"And now, my Young Friend," the coyote said, breaking into her thoughts, "it is time for us to go and begin to spread the word from one end of the valley to the other. You won't be seeing much of us after tonight. We will explain the plan to all the animals of the valley and convince them to work with us. Then we will go underground to save our strength for the hard days that lie ahead. So farewell, and know that you have our deepest thanks for bringing us your warning. Now I have brought you something to quiet the turmoil of your thoughts and to help you sleep."

With that, the old coyote picked up the piece of bark he had brought and, stepping around the fire, laid it gently in Carrie's hand. "Chew this," he said, "as much of it as you can, and hold the juice that comes from it in your mouth. It is a medicine the Indians borrowed from the coyotes in the old times."

Then he touched Carrie's nose with his, and for a moment the look of wildness went out of his glowing amber eyes. They became a single disk of golden light that grew larger and larger as it came toward Carrie, first to her, and then around her. She was floating in it without a body. Then, with an outstretched beat of eagle wings, she circled upward and upward to the top of the sky. From there she saw all the tiny things on earth with such sharpness she felt she could reach out and touch them without effort.

Down she plunged through a rushing tunnel of icy air. Then it grew warm and had a heavy, damp smell. Now, furred, and frightened, she huddled at the mouth of a burrow. Suddenly she pushed against swift cold water, propelled by the surging power of her silver length. With claws extended, she sprang into the midst of scattering quail. The voice of a bobcat filled her throat,

only to become the long drawn-out note of a coyote's howl. In a cold night wind she reached her arms as wide as they would go while the dry leaves whirled and fell about her. The golden light spun and dissolved. Carrie looked into the old coyote's eyes once more and knew that the kinship was complete.

"Ah, yes," he said. "I see you know me now. We will meet again, but until then, I must bid you farewell, my Sister." And the old coyote turned to go.

One by one each of the waiting animals passed Carrie. Some of them touched her jacket or her hand. With each one there was a brief meeting of eyes. Only the lion licked Carrie's face, and she was thrilled by the touch of his rough tongue and the strange smell of his breath. The last of the coyotes brushed the ground of the meeting place with their tails before they disappeared into the shadows of the rocks. Then they were all gone without a trace.

Such terrible aloneness—Carrie felt the tears well up and fall on her hand. The piece of bark she held in it was all that was left. The fire and the moon were nearly gone, and she sat for a while in the darkness without moving.

Hardly knowing what she was doing, Carrie got up to put a few more branches on the embers. Picking up her stone coyote, she slipped into her sleeping bag. It seemed a long time before she stopped shivering and was warm inside the down. While her head whirled in a turmoil of thoughts and visions, she held her coyote close to her chest and began to chew the bitter bark. In her hand she could feel the heart of the coyote beating with her own.

# A Knowing Smile

Before Carrie opened her eyes again, she knew that it was light and that she was no longer in the Valley of the Moon.

She could hear voices as though they were coming from a great distance, and she floated between a desire to inform herself and a desire to sleep and dream forever.

In this half-world her body seemed to grow heavier, and she began to feel an aching pain in every part of herself.

"It's all right, Carrie. You're going to be fine." She recognized her mother's voice and saw her face close above her own. She felt the touch of her mother's hand on her forehead. "You're safe at home, Carrie, right in your own bed."

Now her father was down beside the bed with his face next to hers. Carrie began to cry silently and felt the pillow grow wet beneath her face.

Her father raised his head and shook Carrie's shoulder lightly. "Listen, Carrie," he said. "There's something I want you to know. There isn't going to be any coyote hunt, now or ever."

Memory and realization came back in a blinding light, and Carrie was overcome with feelings of relief and joy. Her silent tears became great heaving sobs while her father held her close and said, "You're all right, baby," over and over again.

The last thing she remembered before she went back to sleep was her mother saying gently, "Better let her rest now, Gordon; she's still a very sick girl."

That part of her recovery she remembered. The details of her rescue she found out only from being told.

It was Blue showing up with his bridle reins hanging the next morning that made Carrie's parents realize that something was wrong.

The first thing Gordon did was to locate Foster through the State Office of Fish and Game, and he was there by that afternoon. It was Foster who guessed where Carrie had gone and tracked her with his hounds.

Carrie was delirious and wandering around when they found her. She had been violently sick to her stomach and was suffering from shock and exposure.

Foster came into her room the next afternoon as she lay half asleep. His dried-leaf face was cracked into a smile, and he brought the smell of the hills in with him.

Carrie realized that this was the first time Foster had ever been to the ranch when the feed was green, and she had a funny feeling that somehow his clothes should have turned green along with it. She laughed and told him so.

It was Foster who told Carrie why she had been so sick. "You know that water gourd you took with you? Well, it wasn't seasoned good enough to drink out of. I guess you thought it seemed dry all right, but it takes sometimes a year or two to get one fit to use. A green gourd's got some kind of poison in it. That is, it's poison if you get too much of it. A long time ago the Indians used to make a sort of tea out of green-gourd water. I've heard tell that it helped them go into a trance and have visions, but not like you, Carrie. I guess you know you come awful close to dying up there."

Foster's voice trailed off to nothing, and he just sat there for a minute with a faraway look in his eyes, before he went on. "Some Indian magic is pretty strong stuff to fool around with if you don't know what you're doing."

It was a quiet warning, followed by a short silence. Then Foster said in a quiet voice, as if to himself, "You know, there's one thing has me puzzled. That piece of bark is what probably saved your life. The old-time Indians used it to counteract the effects of gourd poisoning. I know I never showed any of it to you, because it don't grow around here. It comes from clear up in the Sierra Nevadas.

"And there's another thing, too. I went and took a look in the dump where Leo throwed that coyote he said was half dog and got everybody so stirred up about. She was no such thing at all, just a poor little coyote creature that wasn't made too good in the first place.

Why, that Leo even had the Fish and Game people worried, the mean old wolverine."

Foster gave Carrie a wonderful secret knowing smile, and for the first time she noticed the strange color of his eyes. They were a curious glowing amber, more yellow than brown. He looked right at her for a moment and said, "Best I go now."

Foster never asked Carrie what happened in the Valley of the Moon. She figured it wasn't necessary.

# GLOSSARY

The glossary can help you find out the pronunciations and meanings of some of the words used in this book.

The pronunciation of each word is shown just after the word, in this way: **ab surd** (ab sèrd'). The letters and signs used are pronounced as in the words below. The mark ' is placed after a syllable with primary or heavy accent, as in the example above. The mark ' after a syllable shows secondary or lighter accent, as in **au di to ri um** (ô'də tôr'ē əm).

## FULL PRONUNCIATION KEY*

| | | | | | |
|---|---|---|---|---|---|
| a | hat, cap | j | jam, enjoy | u | cup, butter |
| ā | age, face | k | kind, seek | ù | full, put |
| ä | father, far | l | land, coal | ü | rule, move |
| | | m | me, am | | |
| b | bad, rob | n | no, in | v | very, save |
| ch | child, much | ng | long, bring | w | will, woman |
| d | did, red | | | y | young, yet |
| | | o | hot, rock | z | zero, breeze |
| e | let, best | ō | open, go | zh | measure, seizure |
| ē | equal, be | ô | order, all | | |
| èr | term, learn | oi | oil, voice | ə represents: | |
| | | ou | house, out | | a in about |
| f | fat, if | | | | e in taken |
| g | go, bag | p | paper, cup | | i in pencil |
| h | he, how | r | run, try | | o in lemon |
| | | s | say, yes | | u in circus |
| | | sh | she, rush | | |
| i | it, pin | t | tell, it | | |
| ı | ice, five | th | thin, both | | |
| | | ŦH | then, smooth | | |

*From THORNDIKE–BARNHART INTERMEDIATE DICTIONARY by E. L. Thorndike and Clarence L. Barnhart. Copyright © 1974 by Scott, Foresman and Company. Reprinted by permission of the publisher.

405

# A  a

**ab surd** (ab sėrd'), not sensible; ridiculous.

**ac com plish** (ə kom'plish), to complete successfully; to finish; to carry out.

**a chieve** (ə chēv'), **1** to carry out successfully; to accomplish. **2** to reach by effort.

**ac id** (as'id), any of a class of chemical solutions that are bitter to the taste and turn blue litmus paper red.

**a dapt** (ə dapt'), **1** to make fit; to adjust. **2** to change to fit different situations or conditions.

**al um** (al'əm), a white mineral salt sometimes used as a medicine to stop the bleeding of a small cut.

**am a teur** (am'ə chər *or* am'ə tər), **1** a person who does something for pleasure rather than for pay. **2** a person who is not an expert or is not very skillful.

**an tique** (an tēk'), an object that was made long ago.

**ant ler** (ant'lər), **1** the horn of a deer, elk, or moose. **2** a branch of such a horn.

**ap prais al** (ə prā'zəl), an act of estimating the worth or value of; an evaluation.

**ap pre ci ate** (ə prē'shē āt), **1** to enjoy; to value. **2** to be thankful for.

**ar ray** (ə rā'), an orderly arrangement.

**as cend** (ə send'), to go up; to rise.

**as so ci ate** (ə sō'shē āt), to join or connect in thought.

**au di to ri um** (ô'də tôr'ē əm), **1** a large room for an audience in a public building. **2** a building designed for public gatherings.

**a vi a tor** (ā'vē ā'tər *or* av'ē ā'tər), a pilot or an operator of an aircraft.

# B  b

**balk** (bôk), to stop abruptly and refuse to go on.

**bar ri cade** (bar'ə kād' *or* bar'ə kād), **1** a rough, hastily made barrier or obstruction. **2** to block or obstruct with a barrier.

**bar ri er** (bar'ē ər), an object or objects that stand in the way; an obstacle.

**be card** (bā kärd'), any of several species of thick-billed tropical American birds.

**ben e fit** (ben'ə fit), **1** anything that is for the well-being of a person or thing. **2** a performance or social event to raise money for a worthy cause.

**bi plane** (bī'plān'), an airplane that has two wings on each side, one above the other.

**bo lo tie** (bō'lō), a cord fastened around the neck and worn as a necktie.

**bo ric acid** (bôr′ik), a white, crystalline acid used as a weak antiseptic.

**bro cade** (brō kād′), **1** a fabric woven with raised designs on it. **2** to weave or decorate a fabric with raised designs.

**butte** (byüt), an isolated hill, usually with steep sides and a flattened top.

## C c

**cam ou flage** (kam′ə fläzh), a disguise that will hide something or prevent something from being easily seen.

**can teen** (kan tēn′), **1** a small container, usually with a cloth covering, used to carry water or other drinks. **2** a place of refreshment and recreation for people in military service.

**cap size** (kap sīz′ *or* kap′sīz), to overturn; to turn bottom side up.

**car cass** (kär′kəs), the body of a dead animal.

**car di nal** (kärd′n əl), any of the American finches of which the male has bright-red feathers, a black face, and a pointed crest.

**ca reer** (kə rir′), an occupation or a profession.

**car i bou** (kar′ə bü), any of several large North American deer that are related to the reindeer.

**ce ram ic** (sə ram′ik), **1** of or having to do with the making of earthenware, pottery, or porcelain. **2** an article made of earthenware, pottery, or porcelain.

**char ac ter is tic** (kar′ik tə ris′tik), a special quality or trait that distinguishes one person or thing from another.

**chute** (shüt), **1** a steep slide or passage through which things may pass to a lower level. **2** the rapids in a river. **3** INFORMAL. a parachute.

**ci ta tion** (sī tā′shən), a formal statement of praise or commendation.

**clam ber** (klam′bər), to climb awkwardly using both hands and feet; to scramble.

**cleft** (kleft), an opening or a space made by splitting.

**clin ic** (klin′ik), a place where specific skills or practical instruction on any subject is taught.

**co bra** (kō′brə), a poisonous snake of Asia and Africa that, when excited, flattens and expands its neck so that the head looks like a hood.

---

hat, āge, fär; let, ēqual, tėrm; it, īce; hot, ōpen, ôrder; oil, out; cup, pút, rüle; ch, child; ng, long; sh, she; th, thin; TH, then; zh, measure; ə represents *a* in about, *e* in taken, *i* in pencil, *o* in lemon, *u* in circus.

**col lo di on** (kə lōd′ē ən), a chemical solution that is used to coat photographic film.

**co ma** (kō′mə), a state of prolonged unconsciousness caused by disease or injury.

**com bat** (kom′bat), a fight or struggle.

**com mo tion** (kə mō′shən), a noisy disturbance; confusion.

**com mu ni ca tion** (kə myü′nə kā′ shən), the act of giving or exchanging information.

**com pet i tive** (kəm pet′ə tiv), **1** decided by a contest. **2** having the desire to win.

**com pli cat ed** (kom′plə kā′tid), difficult to understand.

**com pound** (kom′pound), a fenced or walled-in area with buildings inside.

**con trast** (kon′trast), **1** a difference. **2** a person or thing that shows differences when compared with another.

**co or di na tion** (kō ôrd′ n ā′shən), the ability to work together in a smooth way.

**D  d**

**da ta** (dā′tə *or* dat′ə), factual information from which conclusions can be drawn.

**des o late** (des′ə lit), forlorn; dreary; dismal.

**de spair** (di sper′ *or* di spar′), without hope.

**des tine** (des′tən), to cause by fate.

**de vice** (di vīs′), a piece of equipment invented, designed, or fitted for a particular use or special purpose.

**de vour** (di vour′), to eat very hungrily.

**di a gram** (dī′ə gram), a drawing or sketch showing what something is, how it works, or the relation between the parts.

**di lute** (də lüt′ *or* di lüt′), to make thinner or weaker by adding some kind of liquid, such as water.

**dis as ter** (də zas′tər), an event that causes much suffering or loss.

**dis dain ful** (dis dān′fəl), a feeling or showing of scorn.

**dis in te grate** (dis in′tə grāt), to break up or separate into small parts.

**dis may** (dis mā′), a feeling of disappointment or dread.

**drought** (drout), a prolonged period of dry weather.

**E  e**

**em i grant** (em′ə grənt), a person who leaves one country to settle in another.

**em ploy ee** (em ploi′ē *or* em′ploi ē′),
a person who works for another
person or firm for wages.

**e vade** (i vād′), to get away from; to
avoid.

**e vap o rate** (i vap′ə rāt′), to change
from a solid or liquid into a
vapor.

**ex pan sion** (ek span′shən), **1** the
act of being made larger. **2** an
increase in size or volume.

**ex ploit** (ek′sploit), a daring, unusual act.

**F  f**

**feat** (fēt), a remarkable or unusual
deed; an act of courage, skill, or
strength.

**fe tish** (fē′tish *or* fet′
ish), an object be-
lieved to have
magic powers.

**fi ber glass** (fī′bər glas′), a material
made of spun filaments of glass.

**fi nance** (fə nans′ *or* fī′nans), to
raise or provide money for.

**flex i ble** (flek′sə bəl), easily bent
without breaking.

**fre quent ly** (frē′kwənt lē), happening often; every little while.

**fume** (fyüm), smoke, gas, or vapor,
especially if it gives out a strong
odor or is harmful.

**fur nish ings** (fėr′ni shingz),   the
equipment or furniture of a room
or a building.

**G  g**

**gel a tin** (jel′ə tən), a tasteless, odor-
less, jellylike substance, used in
making desserts, glue, or camera
film.

**gen e rate** (jen′ə rāt′), to produce; to
cause to be.

**glimpse** (glimps), **1** a quick view. **2**
to catch a quick view. **3** to look
quickly.

**gloat** (glōt), to think about with
great satisfaction.

**gran ite** (gran′it),   a   hard   rock,
formed by the cooling of melted
rock material.

**guilt y** (gil′tē), having done something wrong.

**gun wale** (gun′l), the upper edge of
a boat's side or a ship's side.

**H  h**

**hack les** (hak′əlz), the hairs on the
back and the neck of a dog or
other such animal, that can become erect.

**hal yard** (hal′yərd), the rope used to
raise or lower a sail or flag on a
ship.

hat, āge, fär; let, ēqual, tėrm; it, īce; hot, ōpen, ôrder; oil, out; cup, pu̇t, rüle; ch, child; ng, long; sh, she;
th, thin; ᴛʜ, then; zh, measure; ə represents *a* in about, *e* in taken, *i* in pencil, *o* in lemon, *u* in circus.

**her pe tol o gist** (hèr′pə tol′ə jist), an expert in the branch of zoology dealing with amphibians and reptiles.

**hurl** (hèrl), to send or thrust with much force.

## I  i

**i den ti cal** (ī den′tə kəl), alike; the same.

**im pact** (im′pakt), the forceful striking of one thing against another.

**im pend ing** (im pen′ding), about to happen; threatening.

**in cline** (in′klīn), a sloping or slanting surface.

**in cred i ble** (in kred′ə bəl), unbelievable; too extraordinary to believe.

**in di ca tion** (in′də kā′shən), 1 the act of making known. 2 a sign or hint of.

**in dig nant** (in dig′nənt), angry because of something mean, unjust, or unworthy.

**in got** (ing′gət), a mass of metal that has been cast into a block or bar to be processed at a later time.

**in ha la tor** (in′ə lat′ər), a device that provides clean air to breathe.

**in stinc tive** (in stingk′tiv), of or having to do with a natural feeling or knowledge.

**in ter i or** (in tir′ē ər), the inside.

## J  j

**jag uar** (jag′wär), a large cat of tropical America that is bigger and heavier than a leopard and has brownish-yellow and black spots.

**ja ve li na** (häv′ə lē′nə), a kind of wild boar found in South America and in the southwest part of the United States.

## K  k

**kay ak** (kī′ak), 1 an Eskimo canoe made of a light frame covered with skins except for a small opening in the middle. 2 a similarly styled boat made of other material.

## L  l

**lank y** (lang′kē), awkwardly tall and thin.

**lei sure ly** (lē′zhər lē), without haste.

**li lac** (lī′lək), a shrub with clusters of fragrant, tiny, pinkish-purple or white blossoms.

**lim it** (lim′it), to keep within restrictions.

## M  m

**ma neu ver** (mə nü′vər), to move skillfully.

**man go** (mang′gō), a juicy, slightly sour, tropical fruit with a thick, yellowish-red rind.

**mar a thon** (mar′ə thon), a long race or contest.

**mar i gold** (mar′ə gōld), a plant with yellow, orange, brownish, or red flowers.

**mas to don** (mas′tə don), any of a large number of extinct mammals similar to present-day elephants.

**mauve** (mōv), pale purple.

**me chan ic** (mə kan′ik), a person skilled with tools, especially one who makes or repairs machines.

**men ace** (men′is), **1** a threat. **2** to threaten.

**mi grant** (mī′grənt), a person, an animal, a bird, or a plant that travels from one place to another.

**min er al** (min′ər əl), a substance, other than a plant or an animal, that is obtained by mining or digging.

**mite** (mīt), a very tiny animal, related to the spider, that lives in foods, on plants, or on other animals.

**molt** (mōlt), to shed feathers or skin before a new growth.

**mon o plane** (mon′ə plān), an airplane with one pair of wings.

**O o**

**o men** (ō′mən), a sign of good fortune or of bad fortune.

**o pin ion** (ə pin′yən), a belief, view, of judgment made by a person.

**P p**

**pa le on tol o gy** (pā′lē on tol′ə jē), a science dealing with the forms of life in prehistoric times, as represented by fossil animals and plants.

**pas tel** (pə stel′), a chalklike crayon used in drawing.

**pe des tri an** (pə des′trē ən), a person who is walking; one who goes on foot.

**pen e trate** (pen′ə trāt), to get into or through.

**plum age** (plü′mij), the feathers of a bird.

**pop u la tion** (pop′yə lā′shən), the number of inhabitants of a given area.

**por tage** (pôr′tij), to carry a boat or provisions from one river or lake to another.

**pre serv a tive** (pri zėr′və tiv), any substance that will prevent injury or decay.

**prow** (prou), the bow, or front part, of a ship or boat.

hat, āge, fär; let, ēqual, tėrm; it, īce; hot, ōpen, ôrder; oil, out; cup, pút, rüle; ch, child; ng, long; sh, she; th, thin; ŦH, then; zh, measure; ə represents *a* in about, *e* in taken, *i* in pencil, *o* in lemon, *u* in circus.

# Q  q

**quail** (kwāl), any of various American game birds belonging to the same family as the pheasant.

**quaint** (kwānt), pleasingly old-fashioned or unusual.

**quest** (kwest), an act of seeking; a search.

# R  r

**raft** (raft), a collection of logs or boards fastened together to make a floating platform.

**rec om men da tion** (rek′ ə men dā′ shən), **1** the act of expressing favorably. **2** anything spoken in favor of a person or thing. **3** a suggestion.

**re gard** (ri gärd′), **1** to consider; to think of. **2** a good opinion; a consideration. **3** to look at closely.

**re lay race** (rē′lā), a race between teams in which a team member covers only a part of the distance.

**rep tile** (rep′təl), any of a class of air-breathing, cold-blooded vertebrates that usually have skin covered with bony plates or scales.

**re tort** (ri tôrt′), to reply quickly or sharply.

**re treat** (ri trēt′), to withdraw; to move back.

**re veal** (ri vēl′), **1** to make known. **2** to show.

**rye** (rī), **1** a hardy annual plant grown for grain. **2** something made from rye grain or flour, such as rye bread.

# S  s

**sac** (sak), a baglike part of a plant or an animal that often contains liquids.

**scut tle** (skut′l), to run swiftly; to scamper.

**se cur i ty** (si kyur′ə tē), the feeling of being safe.

**seep** (sēp), to ooze or trickle through small openings.

**sel dom** (sel′dəm), not happening often; rarely.

**sen ti men tal** (sen′tə men′tl), having or showing tender feeling or emotion.

**sheath** (shēth), **1** a case for the blade of a knife. **2** the covering of part of a plant or an animal.

**shil ling** (shil′ing), a unit of money.

**shoal** (shōl), a sandbar that makes the water in a sea, lake, or stream shallow.

**shuf fle** (shuf′əl), to walk by dragging or sliding the feet.

**site** (sīt), a place or scene.

**smol der** (smōl′dər), a slow burning without flame but with much smoke.

**spar** (spär), a stout, round pole used to support the sails of a ship.

**spec i men** (spes′ə mən), a sample; an item or a part that is typical of a group or a whole.

**sprint** (sprint), a short race run at full speed.

**spunk y** (spung′kē), INFORMAL. full of spirit or courage.

**squad ron** (skwod′rən), a group of eight or more airplanes that fly together.

**strut** (strut), a supporting brace.

**sub merge** (səb mėrj′), to put under or cover with water.

**su per sti tion** (sü′pər stish′ən), a belief or practice resulting from fear of the unknown; mistaken trust in magic or chance.

**sym met ri cal** (si met′rə kəl), having equal proportions in size, shape, and arrangement of parts.

## T t

**tat** (tat), to make a delicate lace by looping and knotting threads with a shuttle.

**tax i der mist** (tak′sə dėr′mist), a person who prepares, stuffs, and mounts animal skins so the animals look alive.

**team ster** (tēm′stər), a person who drives a team of horses or a truck.

**tech ni cian** (tek nish′ən), a person skilled in the details of a science or an art.

**tech nique** (tek nēk′), a special skill or method used to accomplish something.

**ther a py** (ther′ə pē), the treatment of a bodily disorder.

**thong** (thông), a narrow strip of leather.

**tine** (tīn), a projecting point; a prong.

**tor til la** (tôr tē′yə), a flat, round, thin cake made of corn meal usually wrapped around a filling of meat or cheese and eaten hot.

**tour ni quet** (tur′nə ket), a device, such as a bandage that is tightly twisted with a stick, used to stop bleeding.

**trill** (tril), to sing with a trembling, vibrating sound.

**tri pod** (trī′pod), a three-legged stand or support.

**trough** (trôf), a long and narrow channel between waves.

**tur bu lent** (tėr′byə lənt), stormy; violent; causing disturbance.

**tusk** (tusk), a long, pointed, protruding tooth.

**typ i cal** (tip′ə kəl), characteristic of a person, thing, or group.

---

hat, āge, fär; let, ēqual, tėrm; it, īce; hot, ōpen, ôrder; oil, out; cup, pút, rüle; ch, child; ng, long; sh, she; th, thin; ᴛʜ, then; zh, measure; ə represents *a* in about, *e* in taken, *i* in pencil, *o* in lemon, *u* in circus.

## U  u

**u nique** (yü nēk′), **1** the only one of a kind. **2** INFORMAL. unusual or uncommon.

## V  v

**vague** (vāg), not clear or definite; not distinct.

**ven om** (ven′əm), the poison secreted by some snakes, spiders, or other animals.

**ver bal** (vėr′bəl), expressed in spoken words rather than in written words.

**ver te brate** (vėr′tə brit *or* vėr′tə brāt), an animal having a backbone.

**vi sion** (vizh′ən), something seen in one's thoughts, in a dream, or in a trance.

**viv id** (viv′id), bright; brilliant; giving a strong and clear impression.

## W  w

**war y** (wer′ē *or* war′ē), cautious against danger.

**whelp** (hwelp), to give birth to a puppy or cub.

**wol ve rine** (wŭl′və rēn′), a flesh-eating mammal, related to the weasel and badger. It lives in the northern regions of North America.

## Y  y

**yoke** (yōk), a wooden bar or frame that fits around the necks of two work animals to join them together for working.

*(Acknowledgments continued from page 2.)*

Atheneum Publishers, Inc. for the poem "Dinosaurs" by Myra Cohn Livingston. "Dinosaurs" from THE WAY THINGS ARE AND OTHER POEMS by Myra Cohn Livingston (A Margaret K. McElderry Book). Copyright © 1974 by Myra Cohn Livingston. Used by permission of Atheneum Publishers; and for "Trail Boss in Pigtails" by Marjorie Filley Stover. Text copyright © 1972 by Marjorie Filley Stover. From TRAIL BOSS IN PIGTAILS. Used by permission of Atheneum Publishers.

Arthur Catherall for "Twelve Ounces of Courage." Adapted from "Twelve Ounces of Courage" by Arthur Catherall from BOYS' LIFE, October 1970. Reprinted by permission of the author and BOYS' LIFE, published by the Boy Scouts of America.

Crestwood House for "Whitewater Challenge" by Peter B. Mohn. Adapted from WHITEWATER CHALLENGE by Peter B. Mohn, copyright © 1975 by Crestwood House. Used by permission of Crestwood House.

Crown Publishers, Inc. for "You Press the Button, We Do the Rest," by Elizabeth Rider Montgomery. Taken from THE STORY BEHIND GREAT INVENTIONS by Elizabeth Rider Montgomery. Copyright 1944 by Robert M. McBride and Company. Used by permission of Crown Publishers, Inc.

Doubleday & Company, Inc. for "Heroines of the Sky" by Jean Adams and Margaret Kimball. From HEROINES OF THE SKY by Jean Adams and Margaret Kimball, copyright 1942 by Doubleday & Company, Inc. Reprinted by permission of Doubleday & Company, Inc.

Eastman Kodak Company for "How to Make and Use a Cartridge Pinhole Camera." Adapted from *How to Make and Use a Pinhole Camera*, Kodak Publication No. AA-5. Used by permission of Eastman Kodak Company.

Follett Publishing Company for "Little Red" by Burdetta Johnson adapted from LITTLE RED by Burdetta Johnson. Copyright © 1966 by Burdetta Johnson. Used by permission of Follett Publishing Company.

Grosset & Dunlap, Inc. for "Felix the Fourth" by Mac Davis. From STRANGE AND INCREDIBLE SPORTS HAPPENINGS by Mac Davis. Copyright © 1975 by Florence Davis. Used by permission of Grosset & Dunlap, Inc.

Harper & Row, Publishers, Inc. for the poem "Where the Sidewalk Ends" from WHERE THE SIDEWALK ENDS by Shel Silverstein. Copyright © 1974 by Shel Silverstein. Reprinted by permission of Harper & Row, Publishers, Inc.

Hill & Coxe for "Ashu and the Whirlwind" by Erick Berry. Used by permission of O. H. Best and Hill & Coxe.

Alfred A. Knopf, Inc. for the poem "Dreams" by Langston Hughes. From THE DREAM KEEPER AND OTHER POEMS, by Langston Hughes. Copyright 1932 by Alfred A. Knopf, Inc. and renewed 1960 by Langston Hughes. Reprinted by permission of the publisher.

J. B. Lippincott Company for "That Quail, Robert" by Margaret A. Stanger. Adapted from THAT QUAIL, ROBERT by Margaret A. Stanger. Copyright © 1966 by Margaret A. Stanger. Reprinted by permission of J. B. Lippincott Company.

Little, Brown and Company for "Felicia the Critic" by Ellen Conford. Copyright © 1973 by Ellen Conford. From FELICIA THE CRITIC by Ellen Conford, by permission of Little, Brown and Co.; and for "The Incredible Answer-Before-the-Question Trick" by Marilyn Burns. Copyright © 1975 by the Yolla Bolly Press. From THE I HATE MATHEMATICS! BOOK by Marilyn Burns, by permission of Little, Brown and Co.; and for "Sail, Calypso!" by Adrienne Jones. Copyright © 1968 by Adrienne Jones. From SAIL, CALYPSO! by Adrienne Jones, by permission of Little, Brown and Co.

Macmillan Publishing Co., Inc. for "Exploring Crystals" and "Jewels Under a Microscope" by James Berry. Adapted with permission of Macmillan Publishing Co., Inc. from EXPLORING CRYSTALS by James Berry. Copyright © 1964 by James Berry.

Julian Messner for "Cameras and Courage" by Iris Noble. Adapted by permission of Julian Messner, A Division of Simon & Schuster, Inc., from CAMERAS AND COURAGE—Margaret Bourke-White by Iris Noble. Copyright © 1973 by Iris Noble.

*(Acknowledgments continue on page 416.)*

*(Acknowledgments continued from page 415.)*

Minnesota Department of Natural Resources for "In Tune with Our Timber Wolves" by Dave Mech and John Winship. Adapted from "We're in Tune with Our Timber Wolves" by Dave Mech and John Winship from the November/December 1970 issue of *The Minnesota Volunteer,* bimonthly publication of the Minnesota Department of Natural Resources and used with permission.

Virginia Moe, Cook County Forest Preserve District, Trailside Museum, River Forest, Illinois, for helpful information on quail in "That Quail, Robert."

Frank Morelli, Schiller Park, Illinois, for helpful information on quail in "That Quail, Robert."

William Morrow & Co., Inc. for "The Mystery of Pelham House" by Joseph Raskin and Edith Raskin. Reprinted by permission of Lothrop, Lee & Shepard Co., Inc. from TALES OUR SETTLERS TOLD by Joseph Raskin and Edith Raskin. Copyright © 1971 by Joseph Raskin and Edith Raskin; and for "Ocean-Born Mary" by Joseph Raskin and Edith Raskin. Reprinted by permission of Lothrop, Lee & Shepard Co., Inc. from THE NEWCOMERS by Joseph Raskin and Edith Raskin. Copyright © 1974 by Joseph Raskin and Edith Raskin.

Prentice-Hall, Inc. for "Moosik" by Vera Chaplina. From the book TRUE STORIES FROM THE MOSCOW ZOO by Vera Chaplina. © 1970 by Lila Pargment and Estelle Titiev. Published by Prentice-Hall, Inc., Englewood Cliffs, New Jersey.

M. Prutkina, Secretary, and Mr. Igor Sosnovskii, Director, Moscow Zoo, Moscow, U.S.S.R., for photographs used as reference in "Moosik."

Random House, Inc. for "Buddies" by Howard Liss. Adapted by permission of Random House, Inc. from STRANGE BUT TRUE BASKETBALL STORIES, by Howard Liss. Copyright © 1972 by Random House, Inc.

*Reader's Digest* for "The Girl Who Wouldn't Give Up" by Alex Haley. Adapted from The Rotarian (May '61). Copyright 1961 by The Reader's Digest Assn., Inc. Used with permission from Rotary International and The Reader's Digest Assn., Inc.

The Richmond Organization for the poem "Whoopee Ti Yi Yo, Git Along, Little Dogies." GIT ALONG, LITTLE DOGIES Collected, Adapted and Arranged by John A. Lomax & Alan Lomax. TRO—© Copyright 1934 and renewed 1962 LUDLOW MUSIC, INC., New York, N.Y. Used by permission.

Raboo Rodgers for "River of Peril." Adapted from "River of Peril" by Raboo Rodgers from BOYS' LIFE, July 1974. Reprinted by permission of the author and BOYS' LIFE, published by the Boy Scouts of America.

Virginia Driving Hawk Sneve for "The Medicine Bag." Adapted from "The Medicine Bag" by Virginia Driving Hawk Sneve from BOYS' LIFE, March 1975. Reprinted by permission of the author and BOYS' LIFE, published by the Boy Scouts of America.

*Sports Illustrated* for "Showdown on the Tundra" by Ron Rau. Reprinted and adapted courtesy of SPORTS ILLUSTRATED, May 12, 1975. © Time Inc 1975.

The Viking Press, Inc. for "The Indian Heart of Carrie Hodges" by Katy Peake. From THE INDIAN HEART OF CARRIE HODGES by Katy Peake. Copyright © 1972 by Katy Peake. Adapted by permission of The Viking Press.

Franklin Watts, Inc. for "The Hunt for the Mastodon" by Georgianne Ensign, pages 338–347 adapted from THE HUNT FOR THE MASTODON by Georgianne Ensign. Copyright © 1971 by Franklin Watts, Inc. Adapted by permission.

*womenSports* for "Skiing Is Believing" by Linda Joseph. Reprinted by permission of *womenSports* Magazine, January, 1976.

Xerox Education Publications for the poem "Foul Shot" by Edwin A. Hoey from READ Magazine, January 1962. Special permission granted by READ Magazine, published by Xerox Education Publications, © 1962 Xerox Corp.